If this book should ever
rome smack it bum and
send it home
to

Lynne manson
Tor harbgan
sinclair st.
Halkirk

PEARS
Family Quiz Book

Books by Gyles Brandreth

ALADDIN
CINDERELLA
MOTHER GOOSE
DISCOVERING PANTOMIME
I SCREAM FOR ICE CREAM
YAROOH! A FEAST OF FRANK RICHARDS
CREATED IN CAPTIVITY
BRANDRETH'S BEDROOM BOOK
BRANDRETH'S PARTY GAMES
BRANDRETH'S BOOK OF WAITING GAMES
BRANDRETH'S CHRISTMAS BOOK
SCRAMBLED EXITS
COMPLETE BOOK OF HOME ENTERTAINMENT
GAMES FOR TRAINS, PLANES & WET DAYS
THE GENERATION QUIZ BOOK
KNIGHT BOOK OF SCRABBLE
KNIGHT BOOK OF PARTY GAMES
KNIGHT BOOK OF CHRISTMAS FUN
KNIGHT BOOK OF EASTER FUN
KNIGHT BOOK OF HOLIDAY FUN & GAMES
KNIGHT BOOK OF HOSPITAL FUN & GAMES
KNIGHT BOOK OF FUN & GAMES FOR A RAINY DAY
KNIGHT BOOK OF FUN & GAMES FOR JOURNEYS
KNIGHT BOOK OF MAZES
DOMINO GAMES & PUZZLES
NUMBER GAMES & PUZZLES
PAPER & PENCIL GAMES & PUZZLES
GAMES & PUZZLES FOR COINS & MATCHES
HOTCHPOTCH

PEARS
Family Quiz Book
Gyles Brandreth

PELHAM BOOKS

First published in Great Britain by
PELHAM BOOKS LTD
52 Bedford Square,
London WC1B 3EF
November 1976
Second Impression May 1977

© Gyles Brandreth, 1976

Designed by John Elsegood

ISBN 0 7207 0907 5

Printed in Great Britain by
Eyre & Spottiswoode Ltd,
Grosvenor Press, Portsmouth

CONTENTS

INTRODUCTION

When I set sail for my Desert Island, apart from my eight records, my Bible and my Complete Works of William Shakespeare, I will be taking with me a copy of William Makepeace Thackeray's novel *Vanity Fair* and *Alice's Adventures in Wonderland* by Lewis Carroll. Not long ago I would have told you that my two Desert Island books would definitely be those twin feasts of fascinating information, *Pears Cyclopaedia* and *Junior Pears Encyclopaedia,* but my whole life has changed since then.

The reason my whole life has changed, as you've probably guessed, is because I've written this book. And to write this book I've had to read and re-read and almost learn off by heart the entire contents of both *Pears Cyclopaedia* and *Junior Pears Encyclopaedia* ! Every single one of the thousand and more quiz questions you will find in the pages that follow is based on the facts and figures gleaned by me from the *Cyclopaedia* and *Encyclopaedia.* I don't suppose I really *do* know more about absolutely everything than absolutely everybody in the whole wide world, but I must say I *feel* as if I do.

HOW TO USE THE QUIZ BOOK

I wanted to make this a real *family* quiz book, so I have included questions of every kind on all sorts of topics. Half the quizzes have a special theme to them. The other half haven't. Some of the questions are very difficult. Some are very easy. Most are in between.

If you are using the book as a family, get someone to act as quiz master. He can then read out a question at a time and the first person to give the right answer scores a point. If no one knows the answer after the question has been put, the quiz master can then read out the four alternative answers and it will then be the player who picks the right one of the four who scores.

If you are reading the book alone, cover up the alternative answers with your hand and try to answer the question without any help. If you then feel you'd like a clue, look at the four possible answers and try to pick the right one. You will find all the actual answers at the back of the book.

When you score, give yourself two points if you get the answer right without looking at the four alternative answers, but only one point if you get the right answer having seen the alternatives first.

Whatever you score, whoever you are, wherever you come from, I do hope that when you set sail for *your* Desert Island you will be tempted to take a copy of the *Pears Family Quiz Book* with you.

GYLES BRANDRETH

100 QUIZZES

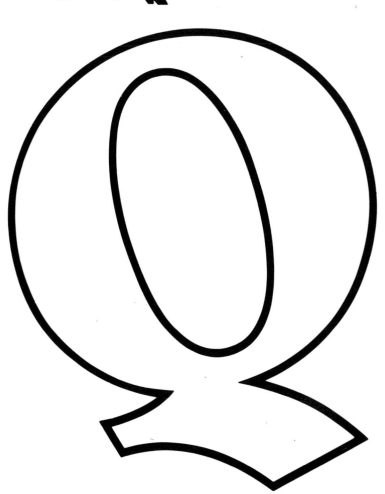

1. **At Christmas what is the everyday name we give to**
    viscum album?
    Is it:
    - a. Holly?
    - b. Ivy?
    - c. Mistletoe?✓
    - d. A Christmas Tree?
2. **With what do you associate the International Sizes marked A0 through to A10?**
    Is it with:
    - a. Liquid?
    - b. Bread?
    - c. Paper?✓
    - d. Hay?
3. **Where will you find** *nu, xi, omicron, rho* **and** *tau?*
    Will it be:
    - a. In Thailand?
    - b. In the Theory of Relativity?
    - c. In the human body?
    - d. In the Greek alphabet? ✓
4. **Who became the Prime Minister of Canada in 1968?**
    Was it:
    - a. Pierre Trudeau?✓
    - b. Alfred Drury?
    - c. Mackenzie King?
    - d. Roland Michener?
5. **Who built the Menai Suspension Bridge?**
    Was it:
    - a. Thomas Telford? ✓
    - b. I. K. Brunel?
    - c. John Richards?
    - d. Jacob Raleigh?

6. **Who was the original illustrator of** *Alice in Wonderland*?
   Was it:
   a. William Hogarth?
   b. Gerald Scarfe?
   c. John Tenniel? ✓
   d. George Cruickshank?

7. **Which English monarch summoned the Model Parliament in 1295?**
   Was it:
   a. Edward I?
   b. Edward II?
   c. Henry I?
   d. Richard II? ✓

8. **In 1939 Britain's largest Opera House was opened. Where was it?**
   Was it in:
   a. Covent Garden?
   b. Manchester?
   c. Edinburgh?
   d. Blackpool? ✓

9. **How was Baron Passfield better known?**
   Was it as:
   a. Charlie Chaplin? ✓
   b. Sidney Webb?
   c. Charles Dickens?
   d. Harold Macmillan?

10. **In what year did 'topless' dresses enjoy a brief vogue in London?**
    Was it in:
    a. 1861?
    b. 1919?
    c. 1964? ✓
    d. 1972?

THE GREAT EXPLORERS

1. **Who discovered Cape Breton Island, Newfoundland and Nova Scotia in 1497?**
   Was it:
   - a. John Cabot?
   - b. Vasco da Gama?
   - c. Christopher Columbus?
   - d. Francis Chichester?

2. **Between 1903 and 1906 who first navigated the North West Passage?**
   Was it:
   - a. Captain James Cook?
   - b. Captain John Speke?
   - c. Captain Roald Amundsen?
   - d. Captain John Smith?

3. **Who discovered Australia in 1606?**
   Was it:
   - a. Henry Hudson?
   - b. William Janszoon?
   - c. William Dampier?
   - d. Ferdinand Magellan?

4. **Who was the *second* man to step onto the moon in 1969?**
   Was it:
   - a. Charles Conrad?
   - b. Frank Borman?
   - c. Jim Lovell?
   - d. Edwin Aldrin?

5. **Who first crossed the Antarctic Continent in 1957-58?**
   Was it:
   - a. Sir Ernest Shackleton?
   - b. Sir James Clark Ross?
   - c. Sir Vivian Fuchs?
   - d. Sir Edmund Hilary?

6. **Who discovered Greenland in 982?**
   Was it:
   - a. Eric the Red?
   - b. Edward the White?
   - c. Cedric the Blue?
   - d. Basil the Black?

7. **What was the name of the ship in which Sir Francis Drake sailed round the world between 1557 and 1580?**
   Was it:
   - a. *The Endeavour*?
   - b. *The Centurion*?
   - c. *The Victory*?
   - d. *The Golden Hind*?

8. **Who reached North America round about the year 1000?**
   Was it:
   - a. Jacques Cartier?
   - b. Christopher Columbus?
   - c. Leif Ericsson?
   - d. Bartholomew Diaz?

9. **Who discovered New Zealand in 1642?**
   Was it:
   - a. Neil Armstrong?
   - b. Martin Frobisher?
   - c. Abel Tasman?
   - d. Richard Chancellor?

10. **Who travelled to Peking in 1255?**
    Was it:
    - a. Joaco Zarco?
    - b. Marco Polo?
    - c. Nicolo Polo?
    - d. Maffeo Polo?

ALLSORTS

1. He was the founder of eugenics, the cousin of Darwin and the man who devised fingerprint identification. What was his name?
   Was it:
   - a. Sir Francis Galton?
   - b. Sir John Spain?
   - c. Sir Edward Rainbow?
   - d. Sir Roland Du Parry?

2. When Laurence Olivier played Othello on stage and screen, who played Iago?
   Was it:
   - a. John Neville?
   - b. Bernard Hepton?
   - c. Frank Finlay?
   - d. Tony Britton?

3. Who was the Greek poet who lived from 310 to 250 BC and whose short poems are called *Idylls*?
   - a Euripides?
   - b. Sophocles?
   - c. Theocritus?
   - d. Thucydides?

4. What is Mrs. Margaret Thatcher's middle name?
   Is it:
   - a. Heather?
   - b. Mary?
   - c. Hilda?
   - d. Marianne?

5. Who created Billy Bunter?
   Was it:
   - a. Charles Hamilton?
   - b. Frank Richards?
   - c. Owen Conquest?
   - d. Frank Drake?

B

6. **Who painted Rouen Cathedral in 1894?**
Was it:
   a. Monet?
   b. Manet?
   c. Dégas?
   d. Toulouse-Lautrec?

7. **Where will you find Poverty Bay and a town called Gisborne?**
In:
   a. England?
   b. Canada?
   c. Zaire?
   d. New Zealand?

8. **When did Sir Henry Wood found the Promenade Concerts?**
Was it in:
   a. 1895?
   b. 1910?
   c. 1918?
   d. 1926?

9. **Who Wrote** *The Silver Tassie*?
Was it:
   a. Sean O'Casey?
   b. J. M. Barrie?
   c. Bernard Shaw?
   d. Oscar Wilde?

10. **What is a phalarope?**
Is it:
   a. A kind of knot?
   b. A kind of anchor?
   c. A kind of crippling disease?
   d. A kind of bird?

1?66

WHEN WAS IT?

1. **When did George Washington become the first President of the United States?**
   Was it in:
   - a. 1776?
   - b. 1789?
   - c. 1814?
   - d. 1899?

2. **When was King John forced to accept the Magna Carta at Runnymede?**
   Was it in:
   - a. 1215?
   - b. 1315?
   - c. 1415?
   - d. 1515?

3. **When did Great Britain get its first Labour Government?**
   Was it in:
   - a. 1904?
   - b. 1924?
   - c. 1945?
   - d. 1964?

4. **When was Napoleon defeated at Waterloo?**
   Was it in:
   - a. 1066?
   - b. 1644?
   - c. 1804?
   - d. 1815?

5. **When did Fidel Castro come to power in Cuba?**
   Was it in:
   - a. 1937?
   - b. 1959?
   - c. 1963?
   - d. 1970?

6. **When was the Siege of Troy?**
   Was it in:
   - a. 1180 BC?
   - b. 222 BC?
   - c. AD 222?
   - d. AD 1180?

7. **When was Robert Bruce crowned King of Scotland?**
   Was it in:
   - a. 579?
   - b. 1306?
   - c. 1491?
   - d. 1564?

8. **When were Dr. Martin Luther King and Robert Kennedy assassinated?**
   Was it in:
   - a. 1960?
   - b. 1963?
   - c. 1966?
   - d. 1968?

9. **When was Joan of Arc burned at the stake?**
   Was it in:
   - a. 1312?
   - b. 1429?
   - c. 1507?
   - d. 1661?

10. **When was the Great Exhibition held in London's Crystal Palace?**
   Was it in:
   - a. 1851?
   - b. 1914?
   - c. 1951?
   - d. 1975?

ALLSORTS

1. **Who became the first Prime Minister of Tanganyika in 1961?**
   Was it:
      a. Julius Nyere?
      b. Idi Amin?
      c. Joshua Nkomo?
      d. Hastings Banda?

2. **In what year did Charles I surrender to the Scots at Newark?**
   Was it in:
      a. 1640?
      b. 1646?
      c. 1652?
      d. 1666?

3. **He was a physicist, the author of** *The Atom* **and, in 1937, a Nobel prize winner. What's his name?**
   Is it:
      a. Sir Thomas Doctorow?
      b. Sir George Thomson?
      c. Sir Raymond Smith?
      d. Sir Laurence Drake?

4. **On American television, who is the host of the** *Tonight* **show?**
   Is it:
      a. Dick Cavett?
      b. David Frost?
      c. Johnny Carson?
      d. Merv Griffin?

5. **Who wrote the play** *Tamburlaine?*
   Was it:
      a. Thomas Kyd?
      b. Ben Jonson?
      c. John Milton?
      d. Christopher Marlowe?

6. **Who was the first Archbishop of Canterbury?**
   Was it:
   - a. St. Augustine?
   - b. St. Thomas Becket?
   - c. St. Aquinas?
   - d. St. Ambrose?

7. **In what year did the Street Offences Act remove prostitution from the British streets?**
   Was it in:
   - a. 1850?
   - b. 1901?
   - c. 1948?
   - d. 1959?

8. **In what British newspaper are the adventures of Rupert Bear featured?**
   In:
   - a. Daily Mirror?
   - b. Daily Mail?
   - c. Daily Express?
   - d. The Guardian?

9. **What is a recidivist?**
   Is it:
   - a. Someone who specialises in market gardening?
   - b. Someone who relapses into crime?
   - c. Someone who is training to be a pastry cook?
   - d. Someone who plans to join the Merchant Navy?

10. **Ponce is the second largest city in a certain American country. Which country?**
    Is it in:
    - a. Puerto Rico?
    - b. Cuba?
    - c. Mexico?
    - d. Canada?

GREAT BATTLES

1. **What was the famous battle that took place in 1415? Was it:**
   a. The Battle of Actium?
   b. The Battle of Agincourt?
   c. The Battle of Austerlitz?
   d. The Battle of Alamein?

2. **What was the famous battle that took place in 1853? Was it:**
   a. The Battle of the Boyne?
   b. The Battle of Barnet?
   c. The Battle of Blenheim?
   d. The Battle of Balaclava?

3. **What was the famous battle that took place in 1746? Was it:**
   a. The Battle of Culloden?
   b. The Battle of Crecy?
   c. The Battle of Copenhagen?
   d. The Battle of Caporetto?

4. **What was the famous battle that took place in 1644? Was it:**
   a. The Battle of Minden?
   b. The Battle of the Marne?
   c. The Battle of Marston Moor?
   d. The Battle of Marengo?

5. **What was the famous battle that took place in 1942? Was it:**
   a. The Battle of Shrewsbury?
   b. The Battle of Sebastopol?
   c. The Battle of Sedgemoor?
   d. The Battle of Stalingrad?

6. **What was the famous battle that took place in 1264? Was it:**
    a. The Battle of Edgehill?
    b. The Battle of Lewes?
    c. The Battle of Poitiers?
    d. The Battle of Trafalgar?

7. **What was the famous battle that took place in 1898? Was it:**
    a. The Battle of Omdurman?
    b. The Battle of Naseby?
    c. The Battle of Wagram?
    d. The Battle of Tewkesbury?

8. **What was the famous battle that took place in 480 BC? Was it:**
    a. The Battle of the Pyramids?
    b. The Battle of Salamanca?
    c. The Battle of Plessey?
    d. The Battle of Thermopylae?

9. **What was the famous battle that took place in 1916? Was it:**
    a. The Battle of Pharsalus?
    b. The Battle of Malplaquet?
    c. The Battle of Jutland?
    d. The Battle of the Nile?

10. **What was the famous battle that took place in 1314? Was it:**
    a. The Battle of Hastings?
    b. The Battle of Bannockburn?
    c. The Battle of Yorktown?
    d. The Battle of Britain?

1. **In what year was Prince Edward born?**
   Was it in:
   a. 1958?
   b. 1964?
   c. 1967?
   d. 1970?

2. **He was a Northamptonshire labourer who became a poet, but died in a lunatic asylum in 1864. What was his name?**
   Was it:
   a. John Keats?
   b. John Clare?
   c. William Wordsworth?
   d. Rupert Brooke?

3. **When England won the World Cup at football in 1966, which country did she beat?**
   Was it:
   a. Italy?
   b. West Germany?
   c. Austria?
   d. Spain?

4. **When Oliver Cromwell ruled England, what was his title?**
   Was it:
   a. King?
   b. Chancellor?
   c. Commander-in-Chief?
   d. Lord Protector?

5. **What is the capital of Albania?**
   Is it:
   a. Tirana?
   b. Prague?
   c. Bucharest?
   d. Kabul?

25

6. **What was the name of the horse that won the Grand National in 1973 and 1974?**
   Was it:
   - a. L'Escargot?
   - b. Red Rum?
   - c. Gay Trip?
   - d. Specify?

7. **If you grew vegetables called King of the Ridge, Stockwood Ridge, Conqueror and Telegraph, what kind of vegetables would you grow?**
   Would they be:
   - a. Potatoes?
   - b. Lettuces?
   - c. Cabbages?
   - d. Cucumbers?

8. **What is the name of the French playwright who lived from 1606 to 1684 and who wrote *Le Cid?***
   Is it:
   - a. Molière?
   - b. Corneille?
   - c. Racine?
   - d. Marivaux?

9. **When Lal Bahadur Shastri died, who succeeded him as Prime Minister of India?**
   Was it:
   - a. Mahatma Gandhi?
   - b. Pandit Nehru?
   - c. Indira Gandhi?
   - d. Solomon Bandaranaika?

10. **In what year did China explode her first nuclear bomb?**
    Was it in:
    - a. 1964?
    - b. 1968?
    - c. 1971?
    - d. 1975?

A FOR ALPHA

1. **Almost everyone knows that, when it comes to radio communication and spelling out words, it's 'A for Alpha', 'B Bravo', 'C Charlie', 'D Delta', and 'E Echo' — but what's the word that goes with F?**
   Is it:
   - a. Fog?
   - b. Fan?
   - c. Fig?
   - d. Foxtrot? ✓

2. **And G?**
   Is it:
   - a. Goat?
   - b. Golf? ✓
   - c. God?
   - d. Golly?

3. **And N?**
   Is it:
   - a. Noddy?
   - b. Never?
   - c. Number?
   - d. November? ✓

4. **And O?**
   Is it:
   - a. Oscar? ✓
   - b. Orange?
   - c. Oliver?
   - d. Orangutang?

5. **And Q?**
   Is it:
   - a. Quiet?
   - b. Queue?
   - c. Question?
   - d. Quebec? ✓

6. **And R?**
   Is it:
   - a. Rudolf? ✓
   - b. Romeo?
   - c. Richard?
   - d. Rabies?
7. **And T ?**
   Is it:
   - a. Tea?
   - b. Tango? ✓
   - c. Tortoise?
   - d. Teapot?
8. **And U?**
   Is it:
   - a. Uniform? ✓
   - b. Underwear?
   - c. Umbrella?
   - d. Uncle?
9.
   And Y?
   Is it:
   - a. Youth?
   - b. Yellow?
   - c. Yes?
   - d. Yankee? ✓
10. **And Z?**
    Is it:
    - a. Zoo?
    - b. Zebra?
    - c. Zulu? ✓
    - d. Zanzibar?

ALLSORTS

1. **Who created Winnie the Pooh?**
   Was it:
   - a. Kenneth Grahame?
   - b. Beatrix Potter?
   - c. A. A. Milne?
   - d. Christopher Robin?

2. **What is the diameter of the sun?**
   Is it:
   - a. About 8,000 miles?
   - b. About 78,000 miles?
   - c. About 864,000 miles?
   - d. About 8,214,000 miles?

3. **What does the Latin exclamation *ecce!* mean?**
   Does it mean:
   - a. Beware of the dog!
   - b. Take care!
   - c. Behold!
   - d. Enough, no more!

4. **What was the religious movement founded by Joseph Smith?**
   Was it:
   - a. Methodism?
   - b. The Society of Friends?
   - c. Mormonism?
   - d. Christian Science?

5. **Who has been the longest reigning British heavyweight boxing champion?**
   Is it:
   - a. Joe Bugner?
   - b. John Conteh?
   - c. Henry Cooper?
   - d. Bob Fitzsimmons?

6. **Where was Lord Snowdon when his separation from Princess Margaret was announced?**
   Was he:
   - a. At Kensington Palace?
   - b. At Buckingham Palace?
   - c. In Cardiff?
   - d. In Australia?

7. **In what year did Owen Glendower assume the title of Prince of Wales?**
   Was it in:
   - a. 1401?
   - b. 1441?
   - c. 1491?
   - d. 1516?

8. **What was the real name of 'Lord Haw-Haw'?**
   Was it:
   - a. James Joyce?
   - b. Inigo Jones?
   - c. William Joyce?
   - d. William Jacobs?

9. **What was the name of the Australian novelist who won the Nobel Prize for Literature in 1973?**
   Was it:
   - a. Richard Black?
   - b. Andrew Brown?
   - c. Terence Green?
   - d. Patrick White?

10. **When did the Rumba become a popular dance?**
    Was it:
    - a. In 1785?
    - b. In 1895?
    - c. In 1935?
    - d. In 1965?

ALL CREATURES GREAT AND SMALL

1. **What's this?**
   Is it:
   - a. An ant-eater?
   - b. A field mouse?
   - c. A shrew? ✓
   - d. A mole?

2. **What's this?**
   Is it:
   - a. A monkey?
   - b. A baboon?
   - c. A sloth? ✓
   - d. A squirrel?

3. **What's this?**
   Is it:
   - a. A bandicoot?
   - b. A tapir? ✓
   - c. A stoat?
   - d. An aardvark?

4. **What's this?**
   Is it:
   - a. A weasel?
   - b. A water vole?
   - c. A platypus? ✓
   - d. A pangolin?

5. What's this?
   Is it:
   - a. An emu? ✓
   - b. A moa?
   - c. A rhea?
   - d. A kiwi?

6. What's this?
   Is it:
   - a. A chaffinch? ✓
   - b. A woodlark?
   - c. A raven?
   - d. A sparrow?

7. What's this?
   Is it:
   - a. A crab?
   - b. A giant prawn?
   - c. A lobster? ✓
   - d. A copepod?

8. What's this?
   Is it:
   - a. A pike?
   - b. A lamprey?
   - c. A skate?
   - d. A carp? ✓

9. What's this?
   Is it:
   - a. A rat kangaroo?
   - b. A kobego?
   - c. A scaly ant-eater? ✓
   - d. An armadillo?

10. What's this?
   Is it:
   - a. A pigmy shrew? ✓
   - b. A tarsier?
   - c. A marsupial mole?
   - d. A rat?

1. **Who wrote a play called** *The Circle*?
   Was it:
   - a. Terence Rattigan?
   - b. Noel Coward?
   - c. Somerset Maugham?
   - d. Emlyn Williams?

2. **In 1968 he sailed round the world single-handed in a boat called the** *Lively Lady*. **What was his name?**
   Was it:
   - a. Alec Rose?
   - b. Francis Chichester?
   - c. Robin Knox-Johnston?
   - d. Edward Heath?

3. **Who was the Roman Emperor who succeeded Caligula?**
   Was it:
   - a. Nero?
   - b. Julius Caesar?
   - c. Augustus Caesar?
   - d. Claudius?

4. **Who starred with Jon Voight in the film** *Midnight Cowboy*?
   Was it:
   - a. Robert Redford?
   - b. Dustin Hofmann?
   - c. Paul Newman?
   - d. Jack Nicholson?

5. **What colour is puce?**
   Is it:
   - a. Purple-brown?
   - b. Blood red?
   - c. Bright orange?
   - d. Cardinal red?

c

6. **Who wrote** *Cautionary Tales* **and** *The Bad Child's Book of Beasts*?
   Was it:
   - a. Edward Lear?
   - b. Lewis Carroll?
   - c. Hilaire Belloc?
   - d. T. S. Eliot?

7. **In what year was Thomas Wolsey created Cardinal and Archbishop of York and appointed Chancellor of England?**
   Was it in:
   - a. 1500?
   - b. 1515?
   - c. 1550?
   - d. 1575?

8. **Who invented the spinning-mule?**
   Was it:
   - a. Samuel Crompton?
   - b. George Shaft?
   - c. Frederick Rowlandson?
   - d. William Baxter?

9. **Where would you go to find Walloons?**
   Would you go:
   - a. To a toyshop?
   - b. To Belgium?
   - c. To a ballet school?
   - d. To a hospital?

10. **Who originated Britain's penny postal service?**
    Was it:
    - a. Sir Cyril Black?
    - b. Sir Robert Mark?
    - c. Sir Rowland Hill?
    - d. Sir Arthur Sullivan?

THE COMMONWEALTH

1. **At the Imperial Conference of 1926 five independent Dominions were described as 'members of the British Commonwealth of Nations'.**
   Which five?
   Were they:
   - a. Australia, Canada, Newfoundland, New Zealand and South Africa?
   - b. Australia, Canada, India, New Zealand and South Africa?
   - c. Australia, Canada, Ghana, Nigeria and Malaysia?
   - d. Australia, Canada, Gibraltar, Malta and the Bahamas?

2. **How many independent countries are now members of the Commonwealth?**
   Is it:
   - a. Five?
   - b. Seventeen?
   - c. Thirty-three?
   - d. Sixty-one?

3. **Which country left the Commonwealth in 1961?**
   Was it:
   - a. South Africa?
   - b. Rhodesia?
   - c. Uganda?
   - d. Botswana?

4. **Malawi and Lesotho are two Commonwealth countries which changed their names on becoming independent.**
   What were they formerly called?
   Were they:
   - a. Nyasaland and Basutoland?
   - b. Tanganyika and Zanzibar?
   - c. Bechuanaland and British Guiana?
   - d. Sierra Leone and Guyana?

5. Which country left the Commonwealth in 1971?
Was it:

      a. India?
      b. Pakistan?
      c. Sri Lanka?
      d. Bangladesh?

6. There is one Commonwealth country in Africa which is still dependent. Which is it?
Is it:

      a. Kenya?
      b. Zambia?
      c. Gambia?
      d. Rhodesia?

7. What do the Commonwealth countries, India, Ghana, Nigeria, Cyprus, Uganda, Kenya, Tanzania, Malawi and Zambia have in common?
Are they:

      a. All members of the 'Old Commonwealth'?
      b. All independent states owing allegiance to the British Crown?
      c. All members of the North Atlantic Treaty Organisation?
      d. All republics?

8. What is the sole dependent Commonwealth territory in the Mediterranean?
Is it:

      a. Cyprus?
      b. Capri?
      c. Gibraltar?
      d. Greece?

9. Who is the Head of the Commonwealth?
Is it:

      a. A different Commonwealth Head of State each year?
      b. A different Commonwealth Head of State every five years?
      c. Always the Queen of England?
      d. President Amin of Uganda until 1978?

10. What is the total population of the Commonwealth?
Is it:

      a. About 52 million?
      b. About 250 million?
      c. About 670 million?
      d. About 950 million?

1. **In the 1974-75 season who were the Football League Champions?**
   Were they:
   - a. Leeds United?
   - b. Derby County?
   - c. Liverpool?
   - d. Arsenal?

2. **In what year did the** *Daily Telegraph* **first appear?**
   Was it in:
   - a. 1790?
   - b. 1855?
   - c. 1900?
   - d. 1932?

3. **When was V.J. Day?**
   Was it:
   - a. 1 January 1900?
   - b. 3 August 1939?
   - c. 15 August 1945?
   - d. 22 November 1963?

4. **How many grains in a pennyweight?**
   Are there:
   - a. 24?
   - b. 48?
   - c. 128?
   - d. 256?

5. **In the Beaufort Scale of Wind Force what does the number 0 signify?**
   Is it:
   - a. Calm?
   - b. Strong gale?
   - c. Storm?
   - d. Hurricane?

6. **In the film of** *My Fair Lady* **who played the part of Eliza?**
   Was it:
   - a. Julie Andrews?
   - b. Barbra Streisand?
   - c. Audrey Hepburn?
   - d. Mary Tyler Moore?

7. **Who was the American Confederate General in the Civil War who made the surrender at Appomattox?**
   Was it:
   - a. General Custer?
   - b. General Dwight Eisenhower?
   - c. General Robert E. Lee?
   - d. General John Leech?

8. **He lived from 1819 to 1895 and in 1857 founded a series of concerts in Manchester that were named after him. What was his name?**
   Was it:
   - a. Sir Charles Hallé?
   - b. Sir Thomas Beecham?
   - c. Sir John Barbirolli?
   - d. Sir Malcolm Sargent?

9. **Who was the Flemish painter who settled in England and became famous for his portraits of Charles I?**
   Was it:
   - a. Sir Anthony Van Dyck?
   - b. Frans Hals?
   - c. Giovanni Bernini?
   - d. Daniel Seghers?

10. **If you were sent a screed, what would you receive?**
    Would it be:
    - a. A plaster duck?
    - b. A sum of money?
    - c. A long letter?
    - d. A tapestry?

WHO WROTE IT?

1. **Who wrote** *Old Wives' Tale*?
   Was it:
   - a. John Buchan?
   - b. Margaret Drabble?
   - c. Arnold Bennett?
   - d. John Galsworthy?

2. **Who wrote** *Morte d'Arthur*?
   Was it:
   - a. Sir John Betjeman?
   - b. Sir Walter Raleigh?
   - c. Sir Walter Scott?
   - d. Sir Thomas Malory?

3. **Who wrote** *The Bab Ballads*?
   Was it:
   - a. W. S. Gilbert?
   - b. Hilaire Belloc?
   - c. T. S. Eliot?
   - d. Ogden Nash?

4. **Who wrote** *Treasure Island*?
   Was it:
   - a. Arthur Conan Doyle?
   - b. Robert Louis Stevenson?
   - c. J. M. Synge?
   - d. H. G. Wells?

5. **Who wrote** *Children of the New Forest*?
   Was it:
   - a. A. A. Milne?
   - b. J. M. Barrie?
   - c. Frederick Marryat?
   - d. T. B. Macauly?

6. **Who wrote** *Piers Plowman*?
   Was it:
   - a. William Langland?
   - b. Geoffrey Chaucer?
   - c. Christopher Marlowe?
   - d. Walter Landor?
7. **Who wrote** *Mill on the Floss*?
   Was it:
   - a. Jane Austen?
   - b. Laurie Lee?
   - c. Mary Ann Evans?
   - d. George Eliot?
8. **Who wrote** *A Shropshire Lad*?
   Was it:
   - a. John Masefield?
   - b. George Herbert?
   - c. John Donne?
   - d. A. E. Housman?
9. **Who wrote** *Paradise Lost*?
   Was it:
   - a. Andrew Marvell?
   - b. John Milton?
   - c. Christina Rossetti?
   - d. Alexander Pope?
10. **Who wrote** *The Alchemist*?
    Was it:
    - a. Ben Jonson?
    - b. Samuel Johnson?
    - c. George Moore?
    - d. Thomas Moore?

1. **What is the musical note that equals half a crotchet? Is it:**
   - a. A quaver?
   - b. A semi-quaver?
   - c. A breve?
   - d. A semi-breve?
2. **When did Switzerland become a full member of the United Nations? Was it:**
   - a. In 1949?
   - b. In 1958?
   - c. In 1964?
   - d. Never?
3. **In 1957 who starred in the film** *Room at the Top*? **Was it:**
   - a. Peter O'Toole?
   - b. Laurence Harvey?
   - c. Richard Burton?
   - d. Laurence Olivier?
4. **In 1381 who led the Peasants' Revolt? Was it:**
   - a. Ben Kingsley?
   - b. Sam Pepys?
   - c. Wat Tyler?
   - d. Guy Fawkes?
5. **He was born in 1887 and died in 1976, having commanded the Eighth Army in North Africa during the Second World War. What was his name? Was it:**
   - a. Lord Wavell?
   - b. Lord Montgomery?
   - c. Lord Napier?
   - d. Lord Mountbatten?

6. **Everest is the world's highest mountain. What is the world's second highest peak?**
   Is it:
   - a. Kanchenjunga?
   - b. Kamet?
   - c. Godwin Austen?
   - d. K2?

7. **In what year did Cyprus become a Republic with Archbishop Makarios as President?**
   Was it in:
   - a. 1955?
   - b. 1959?
   - c. 1967?
   - d. 1973?

8. **By what name is Mozart's Symphony in C better known?**
   Is it:
   - a. The Enigma?
   - b. The Midsummer Night's Dream?
   - c. The Jupiter?
   - d. The Water Music?

9. **Who invented the Morse Code?**
   Was it:
   - a. Gregory Code?
   - b. Samuel Morse?
   - c. Bernard Dacha?
   - d. Andrew Marvell?

10. **She was a world famous Australian soprano who lived from 1861 to 1931. What was her name?**
    Was it:
    - a. Joan Sutherland?
    - b. Rita Hunter?
    - c. Nellie Power?
    - d. Nellie Melba?

LINGUISTICS

1. **What is an anagram?**
   Is it:
   a. A noun that is formed from a verb by adding the letters -*ing*?
   b. A rearrangement of the letters in a word to form another word?
   c. A verb that has no meaning itself but helps to make the meaning of another verb?
   d. A short, sharp, memorable saying?

2. **What is a spoonerism?**
   Is it:
   a. Where you repeat yourself unnecessarily?
   b. Where you use a sentence that doesn't contain a verb?
   c. Where you mix up the initial letters of words?
   d. Where you use over-complicated words to express very simple ideas?

3. **What is litotes?**
   Is it:
   a. Deliberate understatement?
   b. Gross exaggeration?
   c. A form of blank verse?
   d. Another word for a sonnet?

4. **What is a homonym?**
   Is it:
   a. A word that sounds the same as another word but has a different meaning?
   b. A word used to make something sound more attractive than it is?
   c. A name that someone gives themselves that is not really their own?
   d. An abusive adjective?

5. **What is diaresis?**
   Is it:
   - a. An uncontrollable torrent of words?
   - b. The distinction of nouns according to sex?
   - c. The study of the origins of words?
   - d. The pronouncing of two successive vowels in a word as separate sounds?

6. **What is a palindrome?**
   Is it:
   - a. A word that sounds like the noise of an animal?
   - b. A word that is the same in Latin as in English?
   - c. A word that reads the same forwards as backwards?
   - d. A word that can mean several different things at the same time?

7. **What is a simile?**
   Is it:
   - a. Naming something but not by its own name?
   - b. Likening one thing to another?
   - c. Naming the part when you mean the whole?
   - d. Putting a word between the two parts of an infinitive?

8. **What is hyperbole?**
   Is it:
   - a. Exaggeration?
   - b. Unfair emphasis?
   - c. A rhyming pun?
   - d. A cruel joke?

9. **What is alliteration?**
   Is it:
   - a. The intentional use of incorrect spelling?
   - b. The use of words that begin with or include the same letters or sounds?
   - c. The use of words that sound like the things they name?
   - d. The use of ten words when two or three will do?

10. **What is etymology?**
    Is it:
    - a. The part of grammar that deals with the formation of sentences?
    - b. The use of indirect or reported speech?
    - c. The technique of writing in verse or rhyme?
    - d. The study of the origins of words?

ALLSORTS

1. **Britain's new National Theatre opened on the South Bank in March 1976. Of the three auditoria, which was the first opened to the public?**
   Was it:
   - a. The Olivier?
   - b. The Lyttleton?
   - c. The Chandos?
   - d. The Bayliss?

2. **Who was known as 'the lady with the lamp'?**
   Was it:
   - a. Edith Cavell?
   - b. Sheila Scott?
   - c. Florence Nightingale?
   - d. Margot Asquith?

3. **Who was Leader of Britain's Liberal Party before Jeremy Thorpe?**
   Was it:
   - a. David Steel?
   - b. Clement Attlee?
   - c. Jo Grimond?
   - d. Bernard Darwin?

4. **Who wrote *The Wind in the Willows*?**
   Was it:
   - a. A. A. Milne?
   - b. J. M. Barrie?
   - c. John Buchan?
   - d. Kenneth Grahame?

5. **By what name is the plant Helleborus better known?**
   Is it:
   - a. The Michaelmas Daisy?
   - b. The Christmas Rose?
   - c. The Dandelion?
   - d. The Poppy?

6. **What is the name of the cricketer who has made more appearances in Test cricket than any other?**
   Is it:
   - a. Ken Barrington?
   - b. Colin Cowdrey?
   - c. Len Hutton?
   - d. Tom Graveney?

7. **Who played the part of James Bond in the film of** *Doctor No*?
   Was it:
   - a. George Lazenby?
   - b. David Niven?
   - c. Sean Connery?
   - d. Roger Moore?

8. **In 1875, who was the first person to swim the English Channel?**
   Was it:
   - a. Matthew Webb?
   - b. Jacques Cousteau?
   - c. Mark Woolgar?
   - d. John Burns?

9. **Brecht wrote the words of** *The Threepenny Opera*. **Who wrote the music?**
   Was it:
   - a. Gustav Holst?
   - b. Benjamin Britten?
   - c. Kurt Weil?
   - d. Julian Slade?

10. **When Harold Wilson resigned as British Prime Minister, in the election to find his successor who came top of the first poll?**
    Was it:
    - a. Michael Foot?
    - b. James Callaghan?
    - c. Roy Jenkins?
    - d. Denis Healey?

POSTMAN'S LONDON

1. **If you found yourself in E.C.4 where would you be?**
   In:
   - a. Fleet Street? ✓
   - b. Norwood?
   - c. Fulham?
   - d. Hammersmith?

2. **If you found yourself in S.W.5 where would you be?**
   In:
   - a. Clapham?
   - b. Wimbledon?
   - c. Earls Court? ✓
   - d. The City?

3. **If you found yourself in N.10 where would you be?**
   In:
   - a. South Kensington?
   - b. Lewisham?
   - c. New Cross?
   - d. Muswell Hill?

4. **If you found yourself in S.W.17 where would you be?**
   In:
   - a. Bow?
   - b. East Ham?
   - c. Tooting?
   - d. The West End?

5. **If you found yourself in W.2 where would you be?**
   In:
   - a. Paddington?
   - b. Mill Hill?
   - c. Maida Vale?
   - d. Chingford?

6. **If you found yourself in W.4 where would you be? In:**
   - a. Chiswick?
   - b. Covent Garden?
   - c. Chelsea?
   - d. Catford?

7. **If you found yourself in W.8 where would you be? In:**
   - a. Stratford?
   - b. St. John's Wood?
   - c. Kensington?
   - d. Palmer's Green?

8. **If you found yourself in N.17 where would you be? In:**
   - a. Kilburn?
   - b. Mayfair?
   - c. Westminster?
   - d. Tottenham?

9. **If you found yourself in E.3 where would you be? In:**
   - a. Finchley?
   - b. Dulwich?
   - c. Brixton?
   - d. Bow?

10. **If you found yourself in S.W.7 where would you be? In:**
    - a. South Lambeth?
    - b. South Norwood?
    - c. South Kensington?
    - d. Southgate?

1. **Who discovered the circulation of the blood?**
   Was it:
   - a. Louis Pasteur?
   - b. William Harvey?
   - c. Alexander Fleming?
   - d. Benjamin Spock?

2. **What did Pope Pius V do to Queen Elizabeth I of England in 1570?**
   Did he:
   - a. Marry her to Philip of Spain?
   - b. Appoint her Papal Nuncio in England?
   - c. Excommunicate her?
   - d. Award her the Order of the Vatican?

3. **What was Danegeld?**
   Was it:
   - a. A kind of Nordic sweetmeat?
   - b. A kind of poisonous plant?
   - c. A kind of tax?
   - d. A kind of uniform worn after the Norman Conquest?

4. **Who was assassinated in 1865?**
   Was it:
   - a. John Kennedy?
   - b. Abraham Lincoln?
   - c. Martin Luther King?
   - d. Mahatma Gandhi?

5. **Who is the patron saint of Ireland?**
   Is it:
   - a. Saint Seamus?
   - b. Saint Andrew?
   - c. Saint Patrick?
   - d. Saint Eamonn?

D

6. **What is a filibeg?**
   Is it:
   - a. A kilt?
   - b. A disease?
   - c. A shrub?
   - d. A fish?

7. **He designed the R100 airship, the Wellington bomber and the swing-wing aircraft. What's his name?**
   Is it:
   - a. Sir Joshua Reynolds?
   - b. Sir Malcolm Savile?
   - c. Sir Barnes Wallis?
   - d. Sir John Jenkins?

8. **Where is Alsager?**
   Is it:
   - a. In the Alps?
   - b. In Cheshire?
   - c. In the Dordogne?
   - d. In East Germany?

9. **Who was Home Secretary when Clement Attlee was Prime Minister?**
   Was it:
   - a. Herbert Morrison?
   - b. Hugh Dalton?
   - c. Stafford Cripps?
   - d. Chuter Ede?

10. **Whose pseudonym was Q?**
    Was it:
    - a. Peter Quenell?
    - b. Arthur Quiller-Couch?
    - c. Dorothy Quested?
    - d. Queenie Watts?

WHAT'S HIS NAME?

1. **He was the King of the Huns and lived from 406 to 453. What's his name?**
   Is it:
   - a. Earl Attlee?
   - b. Charlemagne?
   - c. Hannibal?
   - d. Attila?

2. **He was the Archbishop of Canterbury who quarrelled with William Rufus, but was a favourite of Henry I. He lived from 1033 to 1109. What's his name? What's his name?**
   Is it:
   - a. St. Thomas Becket?
   - b. St. Thomas Aquinas?
   - c. St. Anselm?
   - d. St. Alban?

3. **He was an American statesman, philosopher and scientist, who lived from 1706 to 1790 and invented the lightning conductor. What's his name?**
   Is it:
   - a. Benjamin Disraeli?
   - b. Benjamin Britten?
   - c. Benjamin Franklin?
   - d. Benjamin Bunny?

4. **He was an American poet who lived from 1819 to 1892 and whose most famous work is called *Leaves of Grass*. What's his name?**
   Is it:
   - a. T. S. Eliot?
   - b. Walt Whitman?
   - c. E. E. Cummings?
   - d. Robert Frost?

5. **In 1892 he became Britain's first Socialist Member of Parliament. What's his name?**
   Is it:
   - a. Stafford Cripps?
   - b. James Keir Hardie?
   - c. Ramsey Macdonald?
   - d. Aneurin Bevan?

6. **He was the first English actor to be knighted for his services to the theatre. What's his name?**
   Is it:
   - a. Sir Herbert Beerbohm Tree?
   - b. Sir Gerald du Maurier?
   - c. Sir Donald Wolfit?
   - d. Sir Henry Irving?

7. **He was a Victorian cricketer who, in the course of his career, scored 54,896 runs and took 2,876 wickets. What's his name?**
   Is it:
   - a. Geoffrey Boycott?
   - b. William Grace?
   - c. Freddie Trueman?
   - d. Gary Sobers?

8. **He was an Austrian psychiatrist and the founder of psycho-analysis. What's his name?**
   Is it:
   - a. Karl Marx?
   - b. Carl Jung?
   - c. Sigmund Freud?
   - d. Friedrich Engels?

9. **He lived from 1624 to 1691 and founded the Quaker movement, the Society of Friends. What's his name?**
   Is it:
   - a. George Fox?
   - b. Brigham Young?
   - c. John Evelyn?
   - d. Martin Luther?

10. **Known as 'the Liberator' he was a revolutionary who broke the Spanish power in South America and became the first President of Venezuela. What's his name?**
    Is it:
    - a. Simon Bolivar?
    - b. Porfirio Diaz?
    - c. Francisco de Miranda?
    - d. Fidel Castro?

1. **Who wrote** *The Moon's a Balloon*? **Was it:**
    a. Desmond Morris?
    b. Jacqueline Suzanne?
    c. Frederick Forsyth?
    d. David Niven?

2. **What did U Thant do between 1962 and 1972? Was he:**
    a. Prime Minister of Burma?
    b. Secretary-General of the United Nations?
    c. President of Thailand?
    d. Director of the British Commonwealth Secretariat?

3. **For what is Paul Valéry remembered? Is it for:**
    a. His pottery?
    b. His sculpture?
    c. His poetry?
    d. His knitting?

4. **Where were the sixteenth Olympic Games held in 1956? Was it in:**
    a. Melbourne?
    b. Munich?
    c. Mexico City?
    d. Montreal?

5. **Who was the last Tsar of Russia? Was it:**
    a. Nicholas I?
    b. Nicholas II?
    c. Alexander II?
    d. Alexander III?

6. **Who kept a diary from 1660 to 1669?**
   Did:
   - a. John Evelyn?
   - b. Charles Greville?
   - c. Harold Nicolson?
   - d. Samuel Pepys?
7. **Who wrote *The Loved One* and *Vile Bodies*?**
   Was it:
   - a. Kingsley Amis?
   - b. Evelyn Waugh?
   - c. Margaret Drabble?
   - d. Hugh Walpole?
8. **For what was Adelina Patti famous?**
   Was it:
   - a. Her singing?
   - b. Her pastry?
   - c. Her piano playing?
   - d. Her splitting of the atom?
9. **What is a grosbeak?**
   Is it:
   - a. A person with a mouth deformity?
   - b. A volcanic eruption?
   - c. A dangerous chemical?
   - d. A type of small bird?
10. **How many members of Parliament can Britain send to the European Parliament in Strasbourg?**
    Is it:
    - a. 10?
    - b. 36?
    - c. 100?
    - d. 140?

HISTORIC ACTS OF PARLIAMENT

1. **What did the Education Act of 1944 do?**
   Did it:
   - a. Introduce elementary education for all?
   - b. Introduce secondary education for all?
   - c. Introduce comprehensive schools for all?
   - d. Introduce university education for all?

2. **What did the Supremacy Act of 1534 do?**
   Did it:
   - a. Make the King of England also King of Scotland?
   - b. Make the King of England also Emperor of India?
   - c. Make the King of England Supreme Head of State?
   - d. Make the King of England Supreme Head of the Church?

3. **What did the Act of Union of 1707 do?**
   Did it:
   - a. Unite England and Ireland?
   - b. Unite England and Scotland?
   - c. Unite England and Wales?
   - d. Unite England and European Economic Community?

4. **What did the Old Age Pensions Act of 1908 do?**
   Did it:
   - a. Introduce old age pensions for the first time?
   - b. Provide pensions for women as well as for men?
   - c. Provide pensions for life for retired Prime Ministers?
   - d. Raise the old age pension from one shilling to two shillings a week?

5. **What did the Parliament Act of 1911 do?**
   Did it:
   - a. Allow members of the House of Lords to disclaim their peerages?
   - b. Provide for the rebuilding of the House of Commons?
   - c. Ban the monarch from presiding over the sittings of Parliament?
   - d. Restrict the powers of the House of Lords?

6. **What did the Toleration Act of 1689 do?**
   Did it:
   - a. Encourage good race relations?
   - b. Allow parents to decide whether or not to send their children to school?
   - c. Establish freedom of worship?
   - d. Set up Speaker's Corner at Hyde Park?

7. **What did the Government Act of 1657 do?**
   Did It:
   - a. Establish Cabinet government?
   - b. Legalise the rule of Oliver Cromwell?
   - c. Order the execution of Charles I?
   - d. State that Parliament had to meet at least once every three years?

8. **What did the Mines Act of 1842 do?**
   Did it:
   - a. Prohibit the employment of ponies, horses and donkeys in mines?
   - b. Prohibit the employment of men over the age of sixty in mines?
   - c. Prohibit the employment of women, girls and boys under ten in mines?
   - d. Prohibit the employment of minors as miners?

9. **What did the Uniformity Act of 1559 do?**
   Did it:
   - a. Force the clergy to use the English Prayer Book?
   - b. Introduce a regulation uniform for all members of the armed services?
   - c. Compel citizens to swear an oath of allegiance to the Crown?
   - d. Encourage the use of school uniforms in grammar schools?

10. **What did the Stamp Act of 1765 do?**
    Did it:
    - a. Introduce postage stamps to Great Britain?
    - b. Impose a tax on legal documents issued within the colonies?
    - c. Introduce the first National Savings Stamps?
    - d. Impose heavy penalties on people who trod on other people's toes?

1. **What was the title of the play by Harold Pinter in which Sir John Gielgud and Sir Ralph Richardson starred in 1975?**
   Was it:
   - a. *Home*?
   - b. *Old Times*?
   - c. *No Man's Land*?
   - d. *The Comedians*?

2. **What is habergeon?**
   Is it:
   - a. A fresh-water fish?
   - b. A sleeveless coat of mail?
   - c. A type of musket?
   - d. A ship's doctor?

3. **Who succeeded Clement Attlee as Leader of the Labour Party in 1955?**
   Was it:
   - a. Harold Wilson?
   - b. James Callaghan?
   - c. Hugh Gaitskell?
   - d. Hugh Dalton?

4. **In which year did Charles I become King of England?**
   Was it in:
   - a. 1625?
   - b. 1630?
   - c. 1635?
   - d. 1640?

5. **With perfect sight, how far can you see at a height of five feet?**
   Is it:
   - a. 2.9 miles?
   - b. 29 miles?
   - c. 298 miles?
   - d. Forever?

6. **After whom is the month of January named?**
Is it:
      a. Queen Jane?
      b. Lady Jane Wellesley?
      c. The Roman god Janus?
      d. The Roman goddess Juno?

7. **When is the Summer Solstice?**
Is it:
      a. On March 21 or 22?
      b. On June 21 or 22?
      c. On September 21 or 22?
      d. On October 21 or 22?

8. **For what is Brendan Foster famous?**
Is it:
      a. For his novels?
      b. For his running?
      c. For his music?
      d. For his researches into micro-biology?

9. **An opera by Mozart has *The Rake Punished* as its English subtitle.**
What's its proper title?
      a. *Cosi fan tutti?*
      b. *Don Giovanni?*
      c. *Die Zauberflöte?*
      d. *La Clemenza di Tito?*

10. **In 1969 the first new decimal coin was circulated in Britain. What was it?**
Was it:
      a. The 1p piece?
      b. The 2p piece?
      c. The 10p piece?
      d. The 50p piece?

THE EARTH

1. **How heavy is the planet Earth?**
   Is it:
   - a. About a million tons?
   - b. About 6,588 million tons?
   - c. About 6,588 million million million tons? ✓
   - d. About 6,588 million million million million million tons?

2. **What is the total surface area of the planet Earth?**
   Is it:
   - a. About a million square miles? ✓
   - b. About 197 million square miles?
   - c. About 197 million million million square miles?
   - d. About 197 million million million million million million square miles?

3. **Quite a bit of the Earth's surface is covered with water. How much?**
   Is it:
   - a. About a quarter?
   - b. About three-eighths? ✓
   - c. About a half?
   - d. About seven-tenths?

4. **The Earth is one of the nine major planets. The others are Mercury, Venus, Mars, Jupiter, Saturn, Uranus, Neptune and Pluto. How does the Earth compare in size with them?**
   Is the Earth:
   - a. The smallest planet?
   - b. The largest planet?
   - c. The fifth largest planet? ✓
   - d. The smallest planet but one?

5. **How far is the Earth from the Sun?**
   Is it:
   - a. About 93,000,000 miles?
   - b. About 93,000,000,000 miles? ✓
   - c. About 93,000,000,000,000 miles?
   - d. About 93,000,000,000,000,000 miles?

6. **The Earth's population is nearing 4,000,000,000. Over half the people live in just one continent. Which one?**
   - a. Europe? ✓
   - b. Africa?
   - c. Asia?
   - d. Oceania?

7. **How much of the land surface of the Earth is uninhabitable?**
   - a. About a quarter? ✓
   - b. About three-eighths?
   - c. About a half?
   - d. About seven-tenths?

8. **What has happened to the Earth's population since the turn of the century?**
   Has it:
   - a. Stayed the same?
   - b. Doubled?
   - c. Trebled?
   - d. Multiplied itself ten times? ✓

9. **On the Earth's surface where will you find an average of over 750 people crowded into each square mile?**
   - a. England? ✓
   - b. Bangladesh? ✓
   - c. Australia?
   - d. Canada?

10. **Which is the Earth's smallest continent?**
    Is it:
    - a. Europe?
    - b. Africa?
    - c. Asia?
    - d. Oceania? ✓

1. **In 1974-75 who won the Football League Cup?**
   Was it:
   a. Aston Villa?
   b. Wolverhampton Wanderers?
   c. Tottenham Hotspur?
   d. Manchester City?

2. **What are the creatures you will find in the reptilian order *Ophidia*?**
   Are they:
   a. Crocodiles?
   b. Lizards?
   c. Turtles?
   d. Snakes?

3. **In which country will you find the River Po?**
   Is it in:
   a. China?
   b. Sri Lanka?
   c. Zambia?
   d. Italy?

4. **She was one of the first women to enter the medical profession and she was the first Englishwoman to hold the office of mayor. What was her name?**
   Was it:
   a. Elizabeth Barrett Browning?
   b. Elizabeth Garrett Anderson?
   c. Elizabeth Sellars?
   d. Elizabeth Rowntree?

5. **What was the name of the heroine of *The Wizard of Oz*?**
   Was it:
   a. Judy?
   b. Alice?
   c. Dorothy?
   d. Amy?

6. **He was Conservative Prime Minister of Great Britain from 1902 to 1905. What was his name?**
   Was it:
       a. Arthur Balfour?
       b. Stanley Baldwin?
       c. Austen Chamberlain?
       d. Neville Chamberlain? ✓

7. **Who wrote the musicals** *Annie Get Your Gun* **and** *Call Me Madam*?
   Was it:
       a. Oscar Hammerstein?
       b. Irving Berlin?
       c. Cole Porter? ✓
       d. Alan Jay Lerner?

8. **He published expurgated editions of Shakespeare and Gibbon for 'family reading'. What was his name?**
   Was it:
       a. William Hazlitt?
       b. Thomas Bowdler?
       c. Kenneth Tynan? ✓
       d. George Meredith?

9. **Who wrote** *Erewhon* **and** *The Way of All Flesh*?
   Was it:
       a. Samuel Johnson? ✓
       b. Samuel Butler?
       c. Anthony Trollope?
       d. Robert Louis Stevenson?

10. **In** *The Slipper and the Rose*, **a film that retold the Cinderella story, who played the part of Prince Charming?**
    Was it:
        a. Robert Redford? ✓
        b. Michael Caine?
        c. Omar Sharif?
        d. Richard Chamberlain?

ENGLISH MONARCHS

1. Who was king before Edward the Confessor?
Was it:
  a. Harold I?
  b. Hardicanute?
  c. Canute?
  d. Ethelred the Unready?

2. Who was the first Plantagenet king?
Was it:
  a. Henry I?
  b. Henry II?
  c. Richard I?
  d. Richard II?

3. Who was the last Tudor monarch?
Was it:
  a. Mary I?
  b. Mary II?
  c. Elizabeth I?
  d. Charles I?

4. Who became king when Henry VI was overthrown in 1461?
Was it:
  a. Edward IV?
  b. Henry VII?
  c. Edward V?
  d. Richard III?

5. Which English king was the Count de Blois?
Was it:
  a. Edgar?
  b. Stephen?
  c. John?
  d. William of Orange?

6. **Which English king belonged to the Royal House of Saxe-Coburg throughout his reign?**
   Was it:
   - a. William IV?
   - b. Edward VII?
   - c. George IV?
   - d. George V?

7. **How long was the reign of Edward VIII?**
   Was it:
   - a. 100 days?
   - b. 325 days?
   - c. 1 year and 17 days?
   - d. 1 year and 315 days?

8. **Who was the first of the Hanoverian kings?**
   Was it:
   - a. William III?
   - b. George I?
   - c. George II?
   - d. William IV?

9. **Who succeeded King John?**
   Was it:
   - a. Richard I?
   - b. Henry II?
   - c. Henry III?
   - d. Edward I?

10. **In what year was Edward V king?**
    Was it in:
    - a. 1483?
    - b. 1485?
    - c. 1509?
    - d. 1603?

1. **Who was President Ford's first Vice-President?**
   Was it:
   - a. Hubert Humphrey?
   - b. Ronald Reagan?
   - c. Henry Kissinger?
   - d. Nelson Rockefeller?

2. **Born in 1758 and guillotined in 1794, he led the Jacobins in the French Revolution. What was his name?**
   Was it:
   - a. Marat?
   - b. Robespierre?
   - c. Saurat?
   - d. Pascal?

3. **Who is the British scientist noted for his work on the chemical structure of the protein insulin?**
   Is it:
   - a. Derek Willoughby?
   - b. Frederick Sanger?
   - c. James Rogers?
   - d. William Matthews?

4. **What was the pseudonym of the French writer Armandine Lucie Dupin who was associated both with Alfred de Musset and Chopin?**
   Was it:
   - a. George Eliot?
   - b. George Sand?
   - c. Georges Simenon?
   - d. George Grossmith?

5. **When was the Union Jack adopted as Britain's national flag?**
   Was it in:
   - a. 1066?
   - b. 1606?
   - c. 1910?
   - d. 1939?

6. **Who created Sooty and Sweep?**
   Was it:
   - a. Harry Worth?
   - b. Harry Belafonte?
   - c. Harry Andrews?
   - d. Harry Corbett?

7. **With what school of philosophy is Jean-Paul Sartre associated?**
   Is it:
   - a. Alchemy?
   - b. Existentialism?
   - c. Utilitarianism?
   - d. Christianity?

8. **Who created Jeeves?**
   Was it:
   - a. Arthur Conan Doyle?
   - b. Bertie Wooster?
   - c. Dorothy L. Sayers?
   - d. P. G. Wodehouse?

9. **What did Alfred Sisley do?**
   Was he:
   - a. A painter?
   - b. A chef?
   - c. A naval captain?
   - d. A French President?

10. **Who founded Methodism?**
    Was it:
    - a. Billy Graham?
    - b. Brigham Young?
    - c. John Wesley?
    - d. James Wyatt?

SCIENCE

1. **For what would you use an altimeter?**
   Would you use it:
   - a. To measure depth beneath the ocean?
   - b. To measure height above the earth?
   - c. To measure sound waves?
   - d. To measure the speed of lightning?

2. **What is an angstrom?**
   Is it:
   - a. An acid?
   - b. An electrode?
   - c. A type of thermometer?
   - d. A unit of length?

3. **What is the meaning of this mathematical sign ≒ ?**
   Does it mean:
   - a. Equal to?
   - b. Not equal to?
   - c. Approximately equal to?
   - d. Marginally less than?

4. **What is the symbol for the chemical element Iron?**
   Is it:
   - a. F?
   - b. I?
   - c. In?
   - d. Fe?

5. **What would you call the positive heavy particle of the nucleus of an atom?**
   Is it:
   - a. A proton?
   - b. A neutron?
   - c. A reagent?
   - d. A volt?

6. What do the initials D.C. stand for?
Is it:
  a. Digital counting?
  b. Direct current?
  c. Dissociation?
  d. Density computer?

7. What is the correct term for a base that is soluble in water?
Is it:
  a. An acid?
  b. An alkali?
  c. A salt?
  d. An oxide?

8. What is an armature?
Is it:
  a. An armchair designed for people with spinal problems?
  b. A standard unit of pressure?
  c. An electrovalent bond?
  d. The coil of an electric motor or dynamo?

9. What is the name of the branch of mathematics that deals with differentiation and integration?
Is it called:
  a. Algebra?
  b. The New Maths?
  c. Calculus?
  d. The Binomial Theorem?

10. What is the symbol for the element gold?
Is it:
  a. G?
  b. Go?
  c. Or?
  d. Au?

1. **In what year was Edward II deposed?**
   Was it in:
   - a. 1327?
   - b. 1357?
   - c. 1427?
   - d. 1457?

2. **The last King of Lydia who died around the year 546 BC is famed for his great wealth. What was his name?**
   Was it:
   - a. Pandora?
   - b. Canute?
   - c. Croesus?
   - d. Solomon?

3. **What is a homograph?**
   Is it:
   - a. A word spelt like another word but with a different meaning?
   - b. A record made for a wind-up gramophone?
   - c. A graph for charting the ebb and flow of tides?
   - d. A type of medicine that relies entirely on herbs?

4. **What is the title of the most famous of the novels of Henry Fielding?**
   Is it:
   - a. *David Copperfield*?
   - b. *Henry Esmond*?
   - c. *Tom Jones*?
   - d. *Lucky Jim*?

5. **On BBC television who presented the original *Tonight* programme?**
   Was it:
   - a. Huw Wheldon?
   - b. Robin Day?
   - c. Richard Dimbleby?
   - d. Cliff Michelmore?

6. **Who introduced the mercury thermometer?**
   Was it:
   - a. André Thermomètre?
   - b. Gabriel Fahrenheit?
   - c. Claude Centigrade?
   - d. James Kirkpatrick?

7. **What happened to Madame Tussaud's Waxworks in 1925?**
   Were they:
   - a. Opened to the public for the first time?
   - b. Visited by the King?
   - c. Burned down?
   - d. Bought by Sir Billy Butlin?

8. **Who discovered the sea route to India in 1498?**
   Was it:
   - a. Marco Polo?
   - b. Vasco da Gama?
   - c. Ferdinand Magellan?
   - d. Thomas Cook?

9. **When it is 12 noon at Greenwich, what time is it in New York?**
   Is it:
   - a. 2.00 am?
   - b. 7.00 am?
   - c. 12 noon?
   - d. 6.00 pm?

10. **As what is Oliver Goldsmith best known?**
    Is it as:
    - a. A goldsmith?
    - b. An explorer?
    - c. A composer?
    - d. A writer?

INTERNATIONAL CURRENCIES

1. **In what country could you use a Lek?**
   In:
       a. Albania?
       b. Bulgaria?
       c. Hungary?
       d. East Germany?

2. **In what country could you use the Baht?**
   In:
       a. Trinidad?
       b. Thailand?
       c. Switzerland?
       d. Japan?

3. **In what country could you use the Balboa?**
   In:
       a. Mexico?
       b. Uganda?
       c. Holland?
       d. Panama?

4. **In what country could you use the Cruzeiro?**
       a. Brazil?
       b. Bolivia?
       c. Tunisia?
       d. Turkey?

5. **In what country could you use the Kwacha?**
   In:
       a. Yugoslavia?
       b. Belgium?
       c. Zambia?
       d. South Africa?

6. **In what country could you use the Gourde?**
   In:
   - a. Peru?
   - b. Sweden?
   - c. New Zealand?
   - d. Haiti?

7. **In what country could you use the Zloty?**
   In:
   - a. Eire?
   - b. Portugal?
   - c. Poland?
   - d. Israel?

8. **In what country could you use the Drachma?**
   In:
   - a. Greece?
   - b. Kenya?
   - c. Algeria?
   - d. Rumania?

9. **In what country could you use the Guilder?**
   In:
   - a. The Netherlands?
   - b. Portugal?
   - c. Iceland?
   - d. Sweden?

10. **In what country could you use the Dollar?**
    In:
    - a. United States of America?
    - b. Australia?
    - c. New Zealand?
    - d. Hong Kong?

1. **What is the flag of the Royal Navy called? Is it:**
   - a. The Red Ensign?
   - b. The White Ensign?
   - c. The Blue Ensign?
   - d. The Royal Standard?

2. **For what is Frank Lloyd Wright famous? Is it as:**
   - a. A sculptor?
   - b. A chemist?
   - c. A President of the United States?
   - d. An architect?

3. **The world's longest tunnel runs for over seventeen miles. Where will you find it? Is it:**
   - a. At Simplon, between Italy and Switzerland?
   - b. At St. Gothard in Switzerland?
   - c. At Ronco in Italy?
   - d. Between East Finchley and Morden in London?

4. **For what is John Curry famous? Is it:**
   - a. His Indian cooking?
   - b. His dress designs?
   - c. His mountaineering?
   - d. His ice skating?

5. **In 1884 what was the record speed for running one mile? The holder was a Briton called George. Was it:**
   - a. 8 minutes 10 seconds?
   - b. 5 minutes 32 seconds?
   - c. 4 minutes 12.75 seconds?
   - d. 3 minutes 59.4 seconds?

6. **Who wrote** *Ode on the Intimations of Immortality*? **Was it:**
    a. William Wordsworth?
    b. John Keats?
    c. Thomas Gray?
    d. Percy Shelley?

7. **What did Thomas Sheraton make? Was it:**
    a. Pottery?
    b. Furniture?
    c. Music?
    d. Railway engines?

8. **Who commanded the 14th Army in Burma, was Chief of the Imperial General Staff from 1948 to 1952 and Governor-General of Australia from 1953 to 1960? Was it:**
    a. Sir Robert Menzies?
    b. Earl Alexander of Tunis?
    c. Viscount Slim?
    d. Lord Wavell?

9. **When did Theodore Roosevelt become President of the United States? Was it in:**
    a. 1904?
    b. 1914?
    c. 1924?
    d. 1934?

10. **Who played Hamlet at Britain's new National Theatre in 1976? Was it:**
    a. Tom Courtenay?
    b. Alan Bates?
    c. Albert Finney?
    d. David Warner?

ISLANDS

1. **Which is the world's largest island?**
   Is it:
   - a. Australia?
   - b. Greenland?
   - c. Borneo?
   - d. New Guinea?

2. **Baffin Island is the fifth largest island in the world. In which ocean is it situated?**
   Is it in:
   - a. The Pacific?
   - b. The Atlantic?
   - c. The Indian?
   - d. The Arctic?

3. **Great Britain is the ninth largest island in the world. What is its area?**
   Is it:
   - a. 2,948,366 square miles?
   - b. 839,782 square miles?
   - c. 161,612 square miles?
   - d. 84,186 square miles?

4. **Which is the largest island in Asia?**
   Is it:
   - a. Sumatra?
   - b. Honshu?
   - c. Java?
   - d. Borneo?

5. **Which is the largest island in Europe?**
   Is it:
   - a. Ireland?
   - b. Iceland?
   - c. Great Britain?
   - d. Elba?

6. **Which is the largest of the four main Channel Islands?**
   Is it:
   - a. Guernsey?
   - b. Jersey?
   - c. Alderney?
   - d. Sark?

7. **The pear-shaped island of Sri Lanka once had a different name.**
   Was it:
   - a. Hispaniola?
   - b. Novaya Zemlya?
   - c. Luzon?
   - d. Ceylon?

8. **To which well-known group do the islands of Brechou, Herm and Jethou belong?**
   Is it:
   - a. The Windward Islands?
   - b. The Canary Islands?
   - c. The Channel Islands?
   - d. The Bahrain Islands?

9. **North Island, South Island, Stewart Island and Chatham Island form a Commonwealth country. Which one?**
   Is it:
   - a. Canada?
   - b. Australia?
   - c. New Zealand?
   - d. Grenada?

10. **There is an island in the Irish Sea between North Lancashire and Northern Ireland. What is it called?**
    Is it:
    - a. The Isle of Dogs?
    - b. The Isle of Man?
    - c. The Isle of Wight?
    - d. The Isle of Ely?

ALLSORTS

1. **What do Sir George Airy and Sir Martin Ryle have in common?**
   Have they both:

   a. Won the Nobel Prize?
   b. Climbed Mount Everest?
   c. Been Astronomer Royal?
   d. Written plays about Oliver Cromwell?

2. **Who was the Chancellor of West Germany from 1949 to 1963?**
   Was it:

   a. Helmut Schmidt?
   b. Willy Brandt?
   c. Konrad Adenauer?
   d. Alfred Adler?

3. **What is a houri?**
   Is it:

   a. A bedtime drink?
   b. A beautiful woman?
   c. A ghost?
   d. An ancient timepiece?

4. **Of what did Prince Albert, the Prince Consort, die?**
   Was it of:

   a. Cancer?
   b. Chicken Pox?
   c. Typhoid Fever?
   d. Influenza?

5. **Who composed *Rule, Britannia*?**
   Was it:

   a. Thomas Tallis?
   b. Thomas Arne?
   c. Edward Elgar?
   d. Edward Heath?

77

6. **Who was the first woman Member of Parliament to take her seat in the British House of Commons?**
   Was it:
   - a. Nancy Astor?
   - b. Barbara Wootton?
   - c. Barbara Castle?
   - d. Margot Asquith?
7. **What did Sir Squire Bancroft do for a living?**
   Was he:
   - a. A chemist?
   - b. An actor-manager?
   - c. A publisher?
   - d. A surgeon?
8. **What happened to Joan of Arc in 1431?**
   Was she:
   - a. Was she born?
   - b. Did she hear her voices for the first time?
   - c. Did she take command of the French forces?
   - d. Was she burnt at the stake?
9. **When was slavery abolished throughout the British Empire?**
   Was it in:
   - a. 1614?
   - b. 1798?
   - c. 1833?
   - d. 1905?
10. **What is the capital of Bangladesh?**
    Is it:
    - a. Accra?
    - b. Delhi?
    - c. Dacca?
    - d. Kabul

ABBREVIATIONS

1. **What does A.P.T. stand for?**
   Is it:
   - a. Advanced Passenger Train?
   - b. Association of Physics Teachers?
   - c. Aerial Programme Technology?
   - d. Armoured Parachute Team?

2. **What does B.A.O.R. stand for?**
   Is it:
   - a. British and Overseas Railways?
   - b. British Advanced Ordnance Research?
   - c. British Architects Order of Rats?
   - d. British Army of the Rhine?

3. **What does Cantab. stand for?**
   Is it:
   - a. Canterbury?
   - b. Mechanical tabulators?
   - c. Cambridge?
   - d. Carthusian?

4. **What does D.B.E. stand for?**
   Is it:
   - a. Dame of the British Empire?
   - b. Dame Commander of the British Empire?
   - c. Dame Commander of the Order of the British Empire?
   - d. Dame Commander of the Order of the British Empire and Commonwealth?

5. **What does K stand for?**
   Is it:
   - a. Kilometre?
   - b. Knight Bachelor?
   - c. King?
   - d. Kelvin?

6. **What does M.F.H. stand for?**
   Is it:
   - a. Military Field Honours?
   - b. Marshal of the Forces of Hohenzollern?
   - c. Master of the Foxhounds?
   - d. Multi Fahrenheit Heat?
7. **What does P.O.W. stand for?**
   Is it:
   - a. Prince of Wales?
   - b. Prisoner of War?
   - c. Poetry of Whitman?
   - d. Part of Winchester?
8. **What does Toc H stand for?**
   Is it:
   - a. Tocken History?
   - b. Territorial Houseguards?
   - c. Talbot House?
   - d. Doctor Thomas Higham?
9. **What does U.S.S.R. stand for?**
   Is it:
   - a. Union of Soviet Socialist Russia?
   - b. United Soviet Socialist Russia?
   - c. Union of Socialist Soviets and Republics?
   - d. Union of Soviet Socialist Republics?
10. **What does Ven. stand for?**
    Is it:
    - a. Venereal Disease?
    - b. Venomous?
    - c. Vegetarian?
    - d. Venerable?

1. In Greek mythology, who was the wife of Pluto?
Was it:
   a. Proserpine?
   b. Helen?
   c. Penelope?
   d. Clytemnestra?

2. How many litres are there in a gallon?
Is it:
   a. 4.5434?
   b. 5.4345?
   c. 6.5434?
   d. 11.873?

3. As a footballer he won 108 caps for England. What was his name?
Was it:
   a. Bobby Charlton?
   b. Stanley Matthews?
   c. Bobby Moore?
   d. James McGrory?

4. Who became World Chess Champion in 1969?
Was it:
   a. Boris Spassky?
   b. Tigran Petrosian?
   c. Tony Miles?
   d. Bobby Fischer?

5. In the film *Anne of the Thousand Days* **who played Henry VIII?**
Was it:
   a. Orson Welles?
   b. Keith Michell?
   c. Richard Burton?
   d. Rod Steiger?

F

6. What is a langur?
   Is it:
   - a. An Egyptian coin?
   - b. A Turkish sweet?
   - c. A monkey?
   - d. A desert shrub?

7. Who assassinated President Lincoln?
   Was it:
   - a. John Wilkes Booth?
   - b. James Pope Cassidy?
   - c. Rupert Nathan Roberts?
   - d. Arthur Sharp Smiley?

8. What did Sir David Brewster invent?
   Was it:
   - a. The telescope?
   - b. The short-wave radio?
   - c. The washing machine?
   - d. The kaleidoscope?

9. The Prime Minister of China died in 1976 at the age of 78. What was his name?
   Was it:
   - a. Mao Tse-Tung?
   - b. Le Duc Tho?
   - c. Chou En-Lai?
   - d. Pam Van Dongh?

10. When did Cleopatra become Queen of Egypt?
   Was it in:
   - a. 600 BC?
   - b. 51 BC?
   - c. 7 BC?
   - d. AD 83?

INVENTORS

1. **Who invented the adding machine?**
   Was it:
   - a. Blaise Pascal? ✓
   - b. Benjamin Franklin?
   - c. William Sturgeon?
   - d. Gustav Adding?

2. **Who invented the Bunsen burner?**
   Was it:
   - a. Antoine Lavoisier?
   - b. Nikola Tesla?
   - c. Charles Towney?
   - d. Robert von Bunsen? ✓

3. **Who invented Aspirin?**
   Was it:
   - a. Hermann Dreser? ✓
   - b. Pierre Curie?
   - c. Alessandro Volta?
   - d. Christian Aspirino?

4. **Who invented Logarithms?**
   Was it:
   - a. John Harrison?
   - b. John Doe?
   - c. John Napier?
   - d. John Augustus? ✓

5. **Who invented Radar?**
   Was it:
   - a. William Ramsey?
   - b. Bernard Crick?
   - c. Robert Watson-Watt? ✓
   - d. Andrew Radar-Brown?

6. **Who invented the Thermometer?**
   Was it:
   - a. Isaac Newton?
   - b. Galileo Galilei? ✓
   - c. Humphry Davy?
   - d. Daniel Rutherford?

7. **Who invented the Microphone?**
   Was it:
   - a. Alexander Graham Bell? ✓
   - b. John Logie Baird?
   - c. Alexander Fleming?
   - d. Henry Bessemer?

8. **Who invented the Slide Rule?**
   Was it:
   - a. William Oughtred? ✓
   - b. William Coke?
   - c. William Shakespeare?
   - d. William Tell?

9. **Who invented the Telescope?**
   Was it:
   - a. Telly Savalas?
   - b. Hans Lippershey? ✓
   - c. J. Philip Reis?
   - d. Guglielmo Marconi?

10. **Who invented Nylon?**
    Was it:
    - a. Wallace Carothers? ✓
    - b. Basil Hester?
    - c. Richard Ruvert?
    - d. Nathaniel Nylon?

1. **What was the name of the English landscape painter who was born in 1776 and died in 1837?**
    Was it:
    a. John Constable?
    b. Joseph Turner?
    c. William Turner?
    d. Walter Pater?

2. **What is a noggin?**
    Is it:
    a. A small water rat?
    c. A small Negro slave?
    c. A small mug?
    d. A small spinning wheel?

3. **By what name is Samuel Langhorne Clemens better known?**
    Is it:
    a. John Bunyan?
    b. Ian Fleming?
    c. Graham Greene?
    d. Mark Twain?

4. **What did Wilhelm Konrad von Röntgen discover?**
    Was it:
    a. Nuclear energy?
    b. Viruses?
    c. X-Rays?
    d. Radium?

5. **For what is Luigi Pirandello famous?**
    Was he:
    a. A Church Reformer?
    b. A playwright?
    c. A deep sea diver?
    d. An Olympic gold medallist?

6. **In what year was the Repeal of the Corn Laws?**
   Was it in:
   - a. 1826?
   - b. 1846?
   - c. 1866?
   - d. 1886?

7. **Who painted a famous portrait of Elizabeth II in 1955?**
   Was it:
   - a. Francis Bacon?
   - b. Pietro Annigoni?
   - c. Pablo Picasso?
   - c. Bridget Riley?

8. **When did Great Britain get commercial television?**
   Was it in:
   - a. 1951?
   - b. 1955?
   - c. 1959?
   - d. 1962?

9. **As what is Sir Karl Popper well known?**
   Is it as:
   - a. A philosopher?
   - b. A photographer?
   - c. A zoologist?
   - d. An actor?

10. **He was a French writer and thinker who lived from 1694 to 1778 and was baptised François-Marie Arouet. By what name is he better known?**
    Is it as:
    - a. Molière?
    - b. Racine?
    - c. Voltaire?
    - d. Corneille?

CAPITAL CITIES

1. **What is the capital of Israel?**
    Is it:
    - a. Haifa?
    - b. Jerusalem?
    - c. Tel Aviv?
    - d. Vaduz?
2. **What is the capital of Hungary?**
    Is it:
    - a. Prague?
    - b. Budapest?
    - c. Warsaw?
    - d. Belgrade?
3. **What is the capital of Malta?**
    Is it:
    - a. Rabat?
    - b. Vila?
    - c. Wellington?
    - d. Valetta?
4. **What is the capital of Burma?**
    Is it:
    - a. Rangoon?
    - b. Amman?
    - c. Dacca?
    - d. Seoul?
5. **What is the capital of Zaire?**
    Is it:
    - a. Kinshasa?
    - b. Lusaka?
    - c. Brazzaville?
    - d. Nairobi?

6. **What is the capital of Ecuador?**
    Is it:
    - a. Buenos Aires?
    - b. La Paz?
    - c. Quito?
    - d. Bogota?
7. **What is the capital of Bermuda?**
    Is it:
    - a. Havana?
    - b. Hamilton?
    - c. Nassau?
    - d. Port-of-Spain?
8. **What is the capital of Morocco?**
    Is it:
    - a. Port Louis?
    - b. Lourenco Marques?
    - c. Jamestown?
    - d. Rabat?
9. **What is the capital of Uruguay?**
    Is it:
    - a. Montevideo?
    - b. Lima?
    - c. Caracas?
    - d. Santiago?
10. **What is the capital of Fiji?**
    Is it:
    - a. Kingston?
    - b. Zomba?
    - c. Riga?
    - d. Suva?

1. **When did Great Britain get its first Highway Code? Was it in:**
   - a. 1890?
   - b. 1905?
   - c. 1924?
   - d. 1955?

2. **Who wrote the novels *Pamela* and *Clarissa*? Was it:**
   - a. Samuel Richardson?
   - b. Samuel Johnson?
   - c. Matthew Arnold?
   - d. Tom Arnold?

3. **When was the maiden voyage of the *Queen Elizabeth I*? Was it in:**
   - a. 1936?
   - b. 1946?
   - c. 1956?
   - d. 1966?

4. **What is a whippoorwill? Is it:**
   - a. A kind of cat o'nine tails?
   - b. A type of mountain goat?
   - c. An American bird?
   - d. A Scottish dance?

5. **A twenty-fifth anniversary is marked with silver, a fiftieth with gold. What marks a first anniversary? Is it:**
   - a. Paper?
   - b. Cotton?
   - c. Leather?
   - d. Silk?

6. **What have John Dryden, Nahum Tate, Colley Cibber, Robert Southey and Robert Bridges in common? Have they all:**
   - a. Written best-selling novels?
   - b. Been created Knights Bachelor?
   - c. Been Poet Laureate?
   - d. Been educated at Cambridge University?

7. **What song is most frequently sung in England? Is it:**
   - a. The National Anthem?
   - b. 'For He's a Jolly Good Fellow'?
   - c. 'Auld Lang Syne'?
   - d. 'Happy Birthday To You'?

8. **In what year was Richard II deposed? Was it in:**
   - a. 1377?
   - b. 1399?
   - c. 1414?
   - d. 1488?

9. **How many tonnes will you find in a ton? Is it:**
   - a. 1?
   - b. 1.016?
   - c. 4.732?
   - d. 9.0065?

10. **Who invented the safety match in 1855? Was it:**
    - a. J. E. Lundstom?
    - b. Frank Whittle?
    - c. Alfred Nobel?
    - d. R. Swan Vesta?

TOP CITIES

Here is a list of the twenty largest cities in the world:

Delhi
Tientsin
Los Angeles
London
Bombay
Detroit
Cairo
Seoul
Tokyo
Mexico City
Chicago
Rio de Janeiro
Djakarta
Philadelphia
Moscow
Sao Paulo
New York
Shanghai
Buenos Aires
Peking

Can you put the list in the right order, with the city with the largest population at the top and the one with the smallest at the bottom?

1. **Where and when did the first parking meter appear?**
   Was it in:
   - a. Oklahoma in 1935?
   - b. New York in 1950?
   - c. London in 1955?
   - d. Leicester in 1960?

2. **What is the 'normal' body temperature?**
   Is it:
   - a. 97.8°F?
   - b. 98.2°F?
   - c. 98.4°F?
   - d. 98.6°F?

3. **For what are Kevin Finnegan, John Stracey, John McClusky and Johnny Clark famous?**
   Are they:
   - a. League Division One footballers?
   - b. British Boxing Champions?
   - c. American Golfers?
   - d. Amateur Jockeys?

4. **Which Second World War bomber was nicknamed 'Wimpy'?**
   Was it:
   - a. The Sunderland?
   - b. The Lancaster?
   - c. The Halifax?
   - d. The Wellington?

5. **Who was the Athenian philosopher who wrote the *Republic*?**
   Was it:
   - a. Aristotle?
   - b. Socrates?
   - c. Plato?
   - d. Euripides?

6. **Who was the first Bourbon king?**
   Was it:
   - a. Philip V of Spain?
   - b. Louis XIV of France?
   - c. Henry VIII of England?
   - d. Philip II of Macedonia?

7. **To which order of birds do swans, geese and ducks belong?**
   Is it:
   - a. Anseriformes?
   - b. Apodiformes?
   - c. Galliformes?
   - d. Strigiformes?

8. **How many countries are there in South America?**
   Is it:
   - a. Six?
   - b. Eight?
   - c. Eleven?
   - d. Eighteen?

9. **Which is the brightest star?**
   Is it:
   - a. Sirius?
   - b. Vega?
   - c. Capella?
   - d. Altair?

10. **Who wrote a poem called *The Raven*?**
    Was it:
    - a. Thomas Love Peacock?
    - b. Edgar Allan Poe?
    - c. Walt Whitman?
    - d. Roy Fuller?

TOP TONGUES

Over two thousand different languages are spoken around the world today. Here is a list of the top twenty:

English
French
German
Italian
Spanish
Portuguese
Russian
Urdu
Bengali
Hindi
Arabic
Malay
Javanese
Japanese
Ukrainian
Telegu
Tamil
Cantonese Chinese
Mandarin Chinese
Wu Chinese

Can you put the list in the correct order, with the world's most spoken language at the top?

1. **What is an olio?**
    Is it:
    - a. A mixed dish?
    - b. A terrible smell?
    - c. A type of ship's rudder?
    - d. A kind of hat?

2. **Who wrote the music for** *West Side Story*?
    Was it:
    - a. Leonard Bernstein?
    - b. Noel Coward?
    - c. Frederick Loewe?
    - d. Benjamin Britten?

3. **Where was Napoleon Bonaparte born?**
    Was it in:
    - a. Corsica?
    - b. Elba?
    - c. Saint Helena?
    - d. Paris?

4. **William Shakespeare wrote a play about a King who suffered a severe defeat at Dunsinane. What was the King called?**
    Was he:
    - a. Lear?
    - b. John?
    - c. Macbeth?
    - d. Henry V?

5. **Who wrote** *The Compleat Angler*?
    Was it:
    - a. Isaac Newton?
    - b. Izaak Walton?
    - c. Isaac Watts?
    - d. Izaak Kingfisher?

6. **What is the Fahrenheit equivalent of 0° Centigrade? Is it:**
   - a. 0°?
   - b. 16°?
   - c. 32°?
   - d. 451°?

7. **Who was the Roman god of revelry and wine? Was it:**
   - a. Cupid?
   - b. Faunus?
   - c. Saturn?
   - d. Bacchus?

8. **Josip Broz became President of Yugoslavia in 1953. By what name is he better known? Is it:**
   - a. Franco?
   - b. Dubcek?
   - c. Stalin?
   - d. Tito?

9. **For what is Elizabeth Schwarzkopf famous? Is she:**
   - a. A novelist?
   - b. A naturalist?
   - c. An opera singer?
   - d. The first American woman to go into space?

10. **What is the capital of Thailand? Is it:**
    - a. Manila?
    - b. Hong Kong?
    - c. Bangkok?
    - d. Papeete?

BRITISH PRIME MINISTERS

1. **Who was George IV's last Prime Minister?**
   Was it:
   - a. Gladstone?
   - b. Sir Robert Peel?
   - c. The Duke of Wellington?
   - d. Earl Grey?

2. **Who formed the National Government of 1935?**
   Was it:
   - a. Stanley Baldwin?
   - b. David Lloyd George?
   - c. Neville Chamberlain?
   - d. Arthur Bonar Law?

3. **In what year did Sir Alec Douglas-Home become Prime Minister?**
   Was it in:
   - a. 1959?
   - b. 1962?
   - c. 1963?
   - d. 1965?

4. **Who was Queen Victoria's first Prime Minister?**
   Was it:
   - a. Lord North?
   - b. Viscount Melbourne?
   - c. Lord John Russell?
   - d. Earl of Derby?

5. **In what year did Sir Robert Walpole become Prime Minister?**
   Was it in:
   - a. 1721?
   - b. 1760?
   - c. 1804?
   - d. 1822?

G

6. In the twentieth century, who was Britain's longest-serving peacetime Prime Minister?
Was it:

     a. Sir Winston Churchill?
     b. Sir Anthony Eden?
     c. Harold Macmillan?
     d. Sir Harold Wilson?

7. When did Benjamin Disraeli first become Prime Minister?
Was it in:

     a. 1850?
     b. 1868?
     c. 1877?
     d. 1890?

8. When he was Prime Minister to which Party did H. H. Asquith belong?
Was it:

     a. The Liberal Party?
     b. The Conservative Party?
     c. The Labour Party?
     d. The Whig Party?

9. Who was British Prime Minister between 1916 and 1922?
Was it:

     a. Henry Campbell-Bannerman?
     c. Arthur Bonar-Law?
     c. David Lloyd George?
     d. James Ramsay MacDonald?

10. Which British Prime Minister was assassinated in 1812?
Was it:

     a. Lord Grenville?
     b. Spencer Perceval?
     c. Viscount Sidmouth?
     d. Duke of Grafton?

1. **Who won the University Boat Race in 1976?**
   Was it:
   - a. Oxford?
   - b. Cambridge?
   - c. A dead heat?
   - d. Cancelled because of freak storms?

2. **This Venetian painter died in 1576 and among his most famous works are** *Bacchus and Ariadne* **and** *Sacred and Profane Love.* **What's his name?**
   Is it:
   - a. Rubens?
   - b. Titian?
   - c. Gauguin?
   - d. Goya?

3. **Which is Great Britain's longest river?**
   Is it:
   - a. The Thames?
   - b. The Severn?
   - c. The Trent?
   - d. The Great Ouse?

4. **What is a butte?**
   Is it:
   - a. A kitchen utensil?
   - b. A collection of short poems?
   - c. A flat-topped hill?
   - d. A kind of butterfly?

5. **What did Louis Blériot do in 1909?**
   Did he:
   - a. Fly the English Channel?
   - b. Fly the Atlantic Ocean?
   - c. Sail single-handed round the globe?
   - d. Discover the North Pole?

6. **Who wrote** *The Cherry Orchard*?
Was it:
        a. Ivan Turgenev?
        b. Maxim Gorki?
        c. Anton Chekhov?
        d. Percy Thrower?

7. **What were the Christian names of the Brothers Grimm?**
Were they:
        a. Bill and Ben?
        b. Eric and Ernie?
        c. Hans and Christiaan?
        d. Jakob and Wilhelm?

8. **Why is Ian Stewart famous?**
Is he:
        a. A runner?
        b. A trumpeter?
        c. A nuclear physicist?
        d. A racing driver?

9. **What is the total mileage of the world's railway routes?**
Is it:
        a. About 70,000 miles?
        b. About 700,000 miles?
        c. About 7,000,000 miles?
        d. About 70,000,000 miles?

10. **Who founded New College, Oxford, and Winchester School?**
Was it:
        a. Thomas Arnold?
        b. William of Wykeham?
        c. The first Duke of Winchester?
        d. J. H. Badley?

WHAT DID HE DO?

1. **Charles Blondin lived from 1872 to 1936. What did he do? Did he:**
   - a. Fly across the English Channel in 1909?
   - b. Pioneer colour television?
   - c. Write the play *French Without Tears*?
   - d. Cross the Niagara Falls on a tightrope?

2. **Pope Innocent III lived from 1160 to 1216. What did he do? Did he:**
   - a. Excommunicate Henry VIII of England?
   - b. Become the first Pope to visit the Holy Land?
   - c. Initiate the fourth Crusade?
   - d. Build Saint Peter's in Rome?

3. **George Hepplewhite died in 1786. What did he do? Was he:**
   - a. A composer?
   - b. A cabinet maker?
   - c. A scientist?
   - d. An architect?

4. **James Graham, Marquess of Montrose, lived from 1612 to 1650. What did he do? Did he:**
   - a. Raise the Highlands in support of Charles I and Charles II?
   - b. Conspire with Guy Fawkes in the Gunpowder Plot?
   - c. Become Oliver Cromwell's first Lord Chancellor?
   - d. Completely reorganise the English navy and army?

5. **Joseph Priestley lived from 1733 to 1804. What did he do? Did he:**
   - a. Construct the first calculating machine?
   - b. Discover oxygen?
   - c. Invent dynamite?
   - d. Construct the Quantum Theory?

6. **Benedict Spinoza lived from 1632 to 1677. What did he do?**
   Was he:
   - a. A Dutch philosopher?
   - b. An Italian composer?
   - c. A Spanish painter?
   - d. An Austrian poet?

7. **Robert Stevenson lived from 1772 to 1850. What did he do?**
   Did he:
   - a. Design landscaped gardens?
   - b. Write poetry and short stories?
   - c. Build lighthouses?
   - d. Invent the railway engine?

8. **Captain William Kidd lived from 1645 to 1701. What did he do?**
   Was he:
   - a. An explorer who sailed round the world?
   - b. One of the founders of the East India Company?
   - c. A revolutionary who was beheaded at Tower Hill?
   - d. A pirate who was hanged at Execution Dock?

9. **Sir Malcolm Campbell lived from 1885 to 1948. What did he do?**
   Was he:
   - a. Foreign Secretary in Winston Churchill's first Cabinet?
   - b. A racing driver who held land and water speed records?
   - c. Britain's last Viceroy of India?
   - d. The man who first sighted the Loch Ness Monster?

10. **Nathaniel Hawthorne lived from 1804 to 1864. What did he do?**
    Was he:
    - a. An English playwright?
    - b. An Irish statesman?
    - c. An American novelist?
    - d. A Canadian painter?

1. **What was the style of painting made famous by Monet, Renoir and Dégas?**
   Was it:
   - a. Fauvism?
   - b. Cubism?
   - c. Impressionism?
   - d. Surrealism?

2. **What is the first of the Ten Commandments?**
   Is it:
   - a. Thou shalt not kill?
   - b. Thou shalt not steal?
   - c. Thou shalt have no other God but Me?
   - d. Thou shalt not commit adultery?

3. **When is Saint Patrick's Day?**
   Is it:
   - a. 1 March?
   - b. 17 March?
   - c. 23 April?
   - d. 30 November?

4. **What do the initials K.T. stand for?**
   Is it:
   - a. Knight Templar?
   - b. Knight of Trieste?
   - c. Knight of the Thistle?
   - d. Knight of the Tomato?

5. **What is the second name of President Gerald R. Ford?**
   Is it:
   - a. Richard?
   - b. Rupert?
   - c. Roger?
   - d. Rudolph?

6. **What do Nero, Galba, Otho, Vitellius and Titus have in common?**
   Were they all:
   - a. Roman Senators?
   - b. Roman poets?
   - c. Roman generals?
   - d. Roman Emperors?

7. **When were Premium Savings Bonds introduced to Great Britain?**
   Was it in:
   - a. 1888?
   - b. 1919?
   - c. 1956?
   - d. 1964?

8. **If you multiply the square of the diameter by .7854, what will you get?**
   Will it be:
   - a. The area of a square?
   - b. The area of a rhomboid?
   - c. The area of a triangle?
   - d. The area of a circle?

9. **What did the American William Hunt invent in 1849?**
   Was it:
   - a. The safety pin?
   - b. The washing machine?
   - c. The tape recorder?
   - d. The transistor radio?

10. **What kind of creature is Basil Brush?**
    Is he a:
    - a. Teddy Bear?
    - b. Fox?
    - c. Monkey?
    - d. Emu?

OCEANS AND SEAS

1. **There are four oceans on the Earth's surface. Which one is the largest?**
   Is it:
      a. The Pacific Ocean?
      b. The Atlantic Ocean?
      c. The Indian Ocean?
      d. The Arctic Ocean?

2. **The greatest known ocean depth is in the Pacific, just off the Philippines. It is about a mile more than the height of Mount Everest. What is the greatest known ocean depth?**
   Is it:
      a. 17,850 feet?
      b. 22,968 feet?
      c. 30,246 feet?
      d. 35,948 feet?

3. **The average height of the land above sea level is 2,300 feet. What is the *average* depth of the ocean?**
   Is it:
      a. 1,300 feet?
      b. 2,300 feet?
      c. 7,451 feet?
      d. 12,451 feet?

4. **How much of the Earth's surface is covered with water?**
   Is it:
      a. About 14 million square miles?
      b. About 140 million square miles?
      c. About 1,400 million square miles?
      d. About 14 million million square miles?

5. **Which sea is larger than the smallest ocean?**
   Is it:
         a. The Caribbean Sea?
         b. The Mediterranean Sea?
         c. The Baltic Sea?
         d. The East China Sea?

6. **Which is the largest of the Earth's seas?**
   Is it:
         a. The North Sea?
         b. The Mediterranean Sea?
         c. The Malay Sea?
         d. The Andaman Sea?

7. **Why won't you find the Malay Sea marked on the map?**
   Is it because:
         a. It doesn't exist?
         b. It is now called the Sea of Okhotsk?
         c. It is made up of a series of other seas, gulfs and straits?
         d. It was divided into the North Sea and the South Sea by the World Sea Conference of 1888?

8. **Which is the deepest of the world's great seas?**
   Is it:
         a. The Caribbean Sea?
         b. The Mediterranean Sea?
         c. The Bering Sea?
         d. The Red Sea?

9. **Which is the shallowest of the world's great seas?**
   Is it:
         a. The Baltic Sea?
         b. The Black Sea?
         c. The Gulf of Mexico?
         d. Hudson Bay?

10. **What is special about the Caspian Sea?**
    Is it:
          a. A sea surrounded by land?
          b. The smallest sea in the Pacific Ocean?
          c. The only sea that does not contain salt water?
          d. The largest sea in the Atlantic Ocean?

1. **Who was the first King of Italy?**
   Was it:
   - a. Victor Emmanuel I?
   - b. Victor Emmanuel II?
   - c. Garibaldi?
   - d. Constantine I?

2. **In 1971, 1972, 1974 and 1975, who won the Scottish Football Cup?**
   Was it:
   - a. Rangers?
   - b. Aberdeen?
   - c. Celtic?
   - d. Dunfermline?

3. **Who wrote *Persuasion*?**
   Was it:
   - a. Walter Scott?
   - b. Virginia Woolf?
   - c. D. H. Lawrence?
   - d. Jane Austen?

4. **Who designed the tapestry for the rebuilt Coventry Cathedral?**
   Was it:
   - a. David Hockney?
   - b. Henry Moore?
   - c. Barbara Hepworth?
   - d. Graham Sutherland?

5. **What is a piastre?**
   Is it:
   - a. A kind of Italian pizza?
   - b. A Spanish coin?
   - c. A Turkish bath?
   - d. An Indian summer?

6. **Who wrote** *Gulliver's Travels*?
   Was it:
   - a. Daniel Defoe?
   - b. Joseph Addison?
   - c. Jonathan Swift?
   - d. William Blake?

7. **What is the second largest city in Burma?**
   Is it:
   - a. Rangoon?
   - b. Mandalay?
   - c. Tikki?
   - d. Manila?

8. **Who was the singer who starred in the 1976 film** *The Man Who Fell to Earth*?
   Was it:
   - a. Adam Faith?
   - b. Mick Jagger?
   - c. Marc Bolan?
   - d. David Bowie?

9. **In what year was Bonn established as the capital of West Germany?**
   Was it in:
   - a. 1918?
   - b. 1945?
   - c. 1949?
   - d. 1956?

10. **Sir John Suckling invented the game of cribbage, but he is better known for something else. What?**
    Was he:
    - a. A navigator?
    - b. One of the plotters with Guy Fawkes?
    - c. A poet?
    - d. A cabinet maker?

MYTHOLOGY

1. **Aphrodite was what the Greeks called the goddess of love. What was the name the Romans gave her? Was it:**
   - a. Juno?
   - b. Venus?
   - c. Diana?
   - d. Minerva?

2. **What was the name of the beautiful young Greek god who was wounded by a boar and changed into an anemone by Aphrodite? Was it:**
   - a. Eros?
   - b. Apollo?
   - c. Pan?
   - d. Adonis?

3. **What was the name of the nymph who was changed into a laurel-bush to save her from Apollo? Was it:**
   - a. Circe?
   - b. Dido?
   - c. Chloe?
   - d. Daphne?

4. **He was the son of Daedalus, but he flew too near the sun wearing only wings of wax. What was his name? Was it:**
   - a. Jason?
   - b. Mars?
   - c. Odin?
   - d. Icarus?

5. **What was the name of the Greek mountain sacred to the nine Muses?**
Was it:

   a. Parnassus?
   b. Vesuvius?
   c. The Mount of Olives?
   d. Mount of Zion?

6. **What was the name of the beautiful youth who pined away for the love of his own reflection and was turned into a flower?**
Was it:

   a. Narcissus?
   b. Nemesis?
   c. Sisyphus?
   d. Perseus?

7. **Tradition has it that he founded Rome in 753 BC. What was his name?**
Was it:

   a. Theseus?
   b. Romulus?
   c. Priam?
   d. Remus?

8. **He was the king of Sparta and the husband of Helen of Troy. What was his name?**
Was it:

   a. Odysseus?
   b. Paris?
   c. Tantalus?
   d. Menelaus?

9. **There were three goddesses, Euphrosyne, Euryale and Stheno, who were regarded as the bestowers of beauty and charm. What was their collective name?**
Were they called:

   a. The Harpies?
   b. The Satyrs?
   c. The Graces?
   d. The Titans?

10. **Neptune was the Roman god of the sea. What was the name of the Greek god of the sea?**

   a. Cronus?
   b. Poseidon?
   c. Achilles?
   d. Osiris?

1. **What is rappee?**
   Is it:
   - a. A kind of snuff?
   - b. A kind of coin?
   - c. A kind of shirt?
   - d. A kind of seaweed?

2. **When did George III come to the throne?**
   Was it in:
   - a. 1700?
   - b. 1760?
   - c. 1790?
   - d. 1820?

3. **Who wrote** *Roderick Random, Peregrine Pickle* **and**
   Humphrey Clinker?
   Was it:
   - a. Tobias Smollett?
   - b. Laurence Sterne?
   - c. Henry Fielding?
   - d. Samuel Richardson?

4. **Who was the English physicist and novelist who coined**
   the phrase 'The Two Cultures'?
   Was it:
   - a. J. P. Donleavy?
   - b. John Mortimer?
   - c. C. P. Snow?
   - d. A. J. P. Taylor?

5. **Who was the German general who commanded the**
   Afrika Corps during the Second World War and
   committed suicide in 1944?
   Was it:
   - a. Goebbels?
   - b. Himmler?
   - c. Rommel?
   - d. Goering?

6. **Who was the Latin poet who lived from 43 BC to AD 18 and wrote the** *Art of Love*?
   Was it:
   - a. Juvenal?
   - b. Plautus? ⁄
   - c. Ovid?
   - d. Tacitus?

7. **On which of Shakespeare's plays is Verdi's opera** *Falstaff* **based?**
   Is it:
   - a. *Henry IV*?
   - b. *The Merry Wives of Windsor*?
   - c. *Henry VI*?
   - d. *A Midsummer Night's Dream*? ⁄

8. **Who invented the cinematograph?**
   Was it:
   - a. Louis Lumière?
   - b. Jean-Jacques Cinéma? ⁄
   - c. Claude Théâtre?
   - d. Angus Kodak?

9. **How many nautical miles are there to a league?**
   Are there:
   - a. Two?
   - b. Three?
   - c. Ten? ⁄
   - d. Twenty-one?

10. **When did the Boston Tea Party take place?**
    Was it in:
    - a. 1722?
    - b. 1773?
    - c. 1790? ⁄
    - d. 1814?

SPACE TRAVEL

1. **Yuri Gagarin was the first man to travel through space on 12 April 1961. What was his spacecraft called?**
   Was it:
   - a. Vostok I?
   - b. Voskhod I?
   - c. Soyuz I?
   - d. Lunik I?

2. **What was the name of the first American in space?**
   Was it:
   - a. Sheppard?
   - b. Grissom?
   - c. Glenn?
   - d. Carpenter?

3. **The first woman in space was Valentina Tereshkova. When did she make her historic flight?**
   Was it:
   - a. In 1963?
   - b. In 1969?
   - c. In 1972?
   - d. In 1975?

4. **What was the name of the first man to leave a space ship and float freely in outer space. It happened in March 1965.**
   Was it:
   - a. Schirra?
   - b. Lovell?
   - c. Leonov?
   - d. Borman?

5. **Neil Armstrong first went into space in March 1966. What was the name of the spaceship in which he travelled?**
   Was it:
   - a. Freedom 7?
   - b. Gemini 8?
   - c. Apollo 9?
   - d. Skylab 10?

6. **Neil Armstrong and Edwin Aldrin were the first two men to step onto the moon. What was the name of the third member of the lunar mission, who didn't actually step out onto the moon's surface?**
Was it:
   a. McDivitt?
   b. Collins?
   c. Conrad?
   d. Bean?

7. **What was the name of the lunar module that Neil Armstrong and Edwin Aldrin landed on the moon?**
Was it called:
   a. Snoopy?
   b. Charlie Brown?
   c. America?
   d. Eagle?

8. **On 14 May 1973 the Americans launched a special space station. What was it called?**
Was it:
   a. Liberty Bell?
   b. Mariner 6?
   c. Surveyor?
   d. Skylab?

9. **What was the name of the first American to step out into space?**
Was it:
   a. White?
   b. Young?
   c. Scott?
   d. Stafford?

10. **In December 1974 West Germany launched its first space probe. What was the spacecraft called?**
Was it:
   a. Pioneer I?
   b. Zond I?
   c. Luna I?
   d. Helios I?

1. **How many of the American colonies issued the Declaration of Independence on 4 July 1776? Was it:**
    a. Five?
    b. Thirteen?
    c. Nineteen?
    d. Thirty-two?

2. **What was the name of the English architect who designed Marble Arch and the Brighton Pavilion and laid out Regent's Park? Was it:**
    a. Christopher Wren?
    b. Basil Spence?
    c. Inigo Jones?
    d. John Nash?

3. **What was the name of the American Nobel prize-winning novelist who wrote *Babbit* and *Elmer Gantry*? Was it:**
    a. F. Scott Fitzgerald?
    b. Ernest Hemingway?
    c. Sinclair Lewis?
    d. Henry Miller?

4. **What was an orohippus? Was it:**
    a. A prehistoric horse?
    b. A Roman senator?
    c. A Greek hip bath?
    d. An Egyptian funeral?

5. **Who were the makers of the RB.211 Jet engine?**
   Was it:
   - a. Pratt & Whitney?
   - b. Rolls-Royce?
   - c. U.S. General Electric?
   - d. Lockheed?

6. **Who starred in the film of** *Mary Poppins*?
   Was it:
   - a. Goldie Hawn?
   - b. Susan Hampshire?
   - c. Julie Christie?
   - d. Julie Andrews?

7. **Who was the Scottish explorer who discovered the course of the Zambesi, the Victoria Falls and Lake Nyasa?**
   Was it:
   - a. David Livingstone?
   - b. Henry Stanley?
   - c. John Donne?
   - d. Daniel Macdonald?

8. **How many miles must you travel to have gone 10 kilometres?**
   Is it:
   - a. 10?
   - b. 8.75?
   - c. 6.21?
   - d. 3.48?

9. **What is the capital of Malawi?**
   Is it:
   - a. Zinder?
   - b. Zomba?
   - c. Zug?
   - d. Zwolle?

10. **He lived from 1933 to 1967 and wrote** *Loot* **and** *Entertaining Mr. Sloane.* **What was his name?**
    Was it:
    - a. Edward Bond?
    - b. Bernard Kops?
    - c. Peter Nichols?
    - d. Joe Orton?

MUSICAL TERMS

1. **What does** *Allegro* **mean?**
   Does it mean:
   - a. Fast, but not too fast?
   - b. Slow, but not too slow?
   - c. At a walking pace?
   - d. Lively?

2. **What does** *Calando* **mean?**
   Does it mean:
   - a. Becoming louder and louder?
   - b. Becoming quieter and slower?
   - c. Becoming quicker and lighter?
   - d. Becoming bolder and brassier?

3. **What does** *Con Brio* **mean?**
   Does it mean:
   - a. Like a whisper?
   - b. With a light touch?
   - c. With verve and dash?
   - d. Like a funeral march?

4. **What does** *Grazioso* **mean?**
   Does it mean:
   - a. Gleefully?
   - b. Cheerfully?
   - c. Gracefully?
   - d. Grandly?

5. **What does** *Legato* **mean?**
   Does it mean:
   - a. In a martial style?
   - b. Like a polka?
   - c. In a smooth style?
   - d. Like a fugue?

6. **What does** *Lento* **mean?**
   Does it mean:
   - a. In borrowed time?
   - b. In even time?
   - c. Slow?
   - d. Stop?

7. **What does** *Presto* **mean?**
   Does it mean:
   - a. Suddenly?
   - b. Very fast?
   - c. Very slow?
   - d. Vigorously?

8. **What does** *Sotto voce* **mean?**
   Does it mean:
   - a. In a sugary voice?
   - b. In a drunken voice?
   - c. In a whisper?
   - d. Humming?

9. **What does** *Vivace* **mean?**
   Does it mean:
   - a. Lively?
   - b. Solemn?
   - c. Fiercely?
   - d. Smoothly?

10. **What does** *Andante* **mean?**
    Does it mean:
    - a. Very quickly?
    - b. Very slowly?
    - c. In the rhythm of a dance?
    - d. At walking pace?

1. **In whose reign was the Authorised Version of the Bible first published?**
   Was it in the reign of:
   - a. James I?
   - b. James II?
   - c. Elizabeth I?
   - d. Victoria?

2. **In 1868 at Tonbridge in Kent the highest temperature ever recorded in Britain was established. What was it?**
   Was it:
   - a. 80°F?
   - b. 90.7°F?
   - c. 100.5°F?
   - d. 136°F?

3. **Who founded the Ford Motor Company?**
   Was it:
   - a. Gerald Ford?
   - b. Henry Ford?
   - c. Glenn Ford?
   - d. J. Arthur Ford?

4. **Who was the German educational reformer who founded the Kindergarten system?**
   Was it:
   - a. Maria Montessori?
   - b. Friedrich Froebel?
   - c. Karl Hauptmann?
   - d. Adolf Bahnhof?

5. **Who was the legendary Swiss patriot who shot an apple on his son's head?**
   Was it:
   - a. Richard the Lionheart?
   - b. Robin Hood?
   - c. William Tell?
   - d. Robinson Crusoe?

119

6. **Who was Galina Ulanova?**
   Was she:
   - a. The first woman in space?
   - b. The discoverer of Vitamin D?
   - c. A major Russian novelist?
   - d. A great ballet dancer?
7. **Who created Captain Hornblower?**
   Was it:
   - a. C. S. Lewis?
   - b. E. M. Forster?
   - c. C. S. Forester?
   - d. J. D. Salinger?
8. **When Sir Winston Churchill was Prime Minister from 1951 to 1955, who was Chancellor of the Exchequer?**
   Was it:
   - a. R. A. Butler?
   - b. Harold Macmillan?
   - c. Selwyn Lloyd?
   - d. Sir Anthony Eden?
9. **In the Soviet Union who was Premier between 1958 and 1964?**
   Was it:
   - a. Malenkov?
   - b. Bulganin?
   - c. Kruschev?
   - d. Kosygin?
10. **Who was the founder of the Moslem religion?**
    Was it:
    - a. Abdhul Baha?
    - b. Jesus?
    - c. Mohammed?
    - d. Allah?

WEIGHTS AND MEASURES

1. **How many chains in a furlong?**
    Is it:
    - a. Eight?
    - b. Ten?
    - c. Twenty?
    - d. Forty-four?
2. **How many drams in an ounce?**
    Is it:
    - a. Six?
    - b. Sixteen?
    - c. Sixty?
    - d. Eighty-two?
3. **How many centimetres in an inch?**
    Is it:
    - a. 1.01?
    - b. 2.54?
    - c. 3.15?
    - d. 3.88?
4. **How many acres in a square mile?**
    Is it:
    - a. 10?
    - b. 1,760?
    - c. 640?
    - d. 96?
5. **How many gallons in a bushel?**
    Is it:
    - a. Four?
    - b. Six?
    - c. Eight?
    - d. Twelve?

6. **How many feet in a nautical mile?**
    Is it:
    - a. 1,000?
    - b. 1,080?
    - c. 6,080?
    - d. 10,800?

7. **How many litres in a quart?**
    Is it:
    - a. 1.136?
    - b. 2.136?
    - c. 3.136?
    - d. 4.136?

8. **How many pounds in a ton?**
    Is it:
    - a. 2,240?
    - b. 4,440?
    - c. 6,640?
    - d. 8,840?

9. **How many cubic inches in a cubic foot?**
    Is it:
    - a. 144?
    - b. 1,728?
    - c. 8,264?
    - d. 12,858?

10. **How many metres in a mile?**
    Is it:
    - a. 100?
    - b. 1,609?
    - c. 2,577?
    - d. 2,981?

1. **Who invented bifocal lenses?**
   Was it:
   - a. Benjamin Spock?
   - b. Benjamin Franklin?
   - c. William Perkins?
   - d. William Gilbert?

2. **What war lasted from 431 to 404 BC?**
   Was it:
   - a. The First Punic War?
   - b. The Second Punic War?
   - c. The Trojan War?
   - d. The Peloponnesian War?

3. **Who was the first Secretary-General of the United Nations?**
   Was it:
   - a. Dag Hammarskjoeld?
   - b. Trygve Lie?
   - c. Kurt Waldheim?
   - d. U Thant?

4. **What was the name of the Genoese navigator who explored America's east coast in 1509?**
   Was it:
   - a. Christopher Columbus?
   - b. Herman Cortes?
   - c. Sebastian Cabot?
   - d. Jacques Cartier?

5. **What is the capital of Tristan da Cunha?**
   Is it:
   - a. London?
   - b. Edinburgh?
   - c. Cardiff?
   - d. Belfast?

6. **You will find the world's largest active volcano in the Andes. What's it called?**
   Is it:
   - a. Guallatiri?
   - b. Lascar?
   - c. Cotopaxi?
   - d. Cotacachi?

7. **What was Botswana once called?**
   Was it:
   - a. Basutoland?
   - b. Nyasaland?
   - c. Bechuanaland?
   - d. The Gold Coast?

8. **An Admiral in the Royal Navy is the equivalent of a General in the Army. What is their equivalent in the Royal Air Force?**
   Is it:
   - a. Air Commodore?
   - b. Air Vice Marshal?
   - c. Air Marshal?
   - d. Air Chief Marshal?

9. **What is the chemical symbol for copper?**
   Is it:
   - a. Co?
   - b. Cu?
   - c. Cm?
   - d. Cp?

10. **In geometry what would you call a straight line joining two points on the circumference of a circle?**
    Would you call it:
    - a. An arc?
    - b. A chord?
    - c. A radius?
    - d. A sector?

MOTORCARS

1. What's this?
Is it:

 a. A 1926 Austin 7?
 b. A 1927 Model T Ford?
 c. A 1928 Fiat Topolino?
 d. A 1929 Mercedes-Benz?

2. What's this?
Is it:

 a. A Lotus Elite?
 b. A Jaguar XJ6?
 c. A Lamborghini Mark III?
 d. An NSU R080?

3. What's this?
Is it:

 a. A Fiat 128 Coupé?
 b. A Fiat 130 Saloon?
 c. A Ford Consul?
 d. A Ford Escort?

4. What's this?
Is it:

 a. A Rolls-Royce Corniche?
 b. A Rolls-Royce Camargue?
 c. A Rolls-Royce Silver Ghost?
 d. A Rolls-Royce Silver Shadow?

5. What's this?
Is it:

 a. A Volkswagen?
 b. A Fiat 127 Saloon?
 c. A Citroën GS?
 d. A Renault 16 TS?

6. What's this?
   Is it:

   a. A Citroen DS?
   b. A Peugeot Bébé?
   c. A 1937 Lancia?
   d. A 1938 BMW?

7. What's this?
   Is it:

   a. A Riley Falcon?
   b. A Hillman Imp?
   c. A Sunbeam Singer?
   d. A Morris Cowley?

8. What's this?
   Is it:

   a. A Ferrari?
   b. A Lotus Elite?
   c. A Maserati?
   d. A Jensen?

9. What's this?
   Is it:

   a. A Bugatti Model F?
   b. A Du Pont Model G?
   c. A Skoda Model H?
   d. A Panhard Model I?

10. What's this?
   Is it:

   a. A 3-litre Aston Martin?
   b. A 3-litre Daimler?
   c. A 3-litre Lagonda?
   d. A 3-litre Bentley?

1. **Who wrote** *Das Kapital*?
   Was it:
      a. Engels?
      b. Marx?
      c. Freud?
      d. Goethe?

2. **What was the new name given to Saigon in 1975?**
   Was it:
      a. Mao City?
      b. Viet City?
      c. Ho Chi Minh City?
      d. Kong City?

3. **Who created Noddy and Big Ears?**
   Was it:
      a. Agatha Christie?
      b. Michael Bond?
      c. Beatrix Potter?
      d. Enid Blyton?

4. **Who wrote the play** *Cyrano de Bergerac*?
   Was it:
      a. Arthur Wing Pinero?
      b. John Galsworthy?
      c. Jean Anouilh?
      d. Edmond Rostand?

5. **Which English county has become County Cricket Champions more than any other?**
   Is it?
      a. Hampshire?
      b. Yorkshire?
      c. Surrey?
      d. Lancashire?

6. **What is the title of Emily Brontë's only novel?**
   Is it:
         a. *Jane Eyre*?
         b. *Wuthering Heights*?
         c. *Villette*?
         d. *Agnes Grey*?

7. **When Napoleon retreated from Moscow in 1812, of his army of 550,000, how many survived?**
   Was it:
         a. 500,000?
         b. 200,000?
         c. 20,000?
         d. None?

8. **Who invented the water closet?**
   Was it:
         a. Cyril Shanks?
         b. Joseph Bramah?
         c. Winston Cardew?
         d. Louis Brennan?

9. **Who wrote the poem *Granchester*?**
   Was it:
         a. Wilfred Owen?
         b. Robert Graves?
         c. C. Day Lewis?
         d. Rupert Brooke?

10. **In the television series *The Avengers*, who played the first of Steed's girl assistants?**
    Was it:
          a. Linda Thorson?
          b. Joanna Lumley?
          c. Diana Rigg?
          d. Honor Blackman?

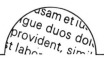

LATIN TAGS

1. **What does** *tempus fugit* **mean?**
   Does it mean:
   - a. The bird has flown?
   - b. Time flies?
   - c. Don't lose your temper?
   - d. He is tempted to escape?

2. **What does** *quod erat demonstrandum* **mean?**
   Does it mean:
   - a. Four mistakes have been shown?
   - b. All is revealed in the courtyard?
   - c. Demonstrate the solution in four ways?
   - d. Which was to be proved?

3. **What does** *nil desperandum* **mean?**
   Does it mean:
   - a. Never despair?
   - b. The enemy will not score?
   - c. The Nile has no source?
   - d. The worst is yet to come?

4. **What does** *exempli gratia* **mean?**
   Does it mean:
   - a. Free sample?
   - b. What a gracious example?
   - c. In this instance?
   - d. By way of example?

5. **What does** *dei gratia* **mean?**
   Does it mean:
   - a. By the grace of God?
   - b. This is a great day?
   - c. Praise be to the Lord?
   - d. O come all ye faithful?

I

6. **What does** *amor vincit omnia* **mean?**
   Is it:
   - a. He who wears armour is invincible?
   - b. He who laughs last laughs longest?
   - c. Love conquers all?
   - d. All the world's a stage?

7. **What does** *hic et ubique* **mean?**
   Is it:
   - a. Hither and thither?
   - b. Many hands make light work?
   - c. Now or never?
   - d. Here and everywhere?

8. **What does** *nolens volens* **mean?**
   Is it:
   - a. No one loves me?
   - b. Mark this well?
   - c. Whether he will or not?
   - d. Steer the straightest course?

9. **What does** *virginibus puerisque* **mean?**
   Is it:
   - a. Of mice and men?
   - b. For boys and girls?
   - c. Hail to the pure virgin?
   - d. The girl has taken a dangerous risk?

10. **What does** *requiescat in pace* **mean?**
    Is it:
    - a. May he rest in peace?
    - b. May he keep up the necessary pace?
    - c. May he live for ever?
    - d. May he have a happy retirement?

ALLSORTS

1. **What was the name of the 101st Archbishop of Canterbury?**
   Was it:
   > a. Michael Ramsey?
   > b. Geoffrey Fisher?
   > c. Donald Coggan?
   > d. Thomas Becket?

2. **Who was the Czech composer who wrote a symphony in E minor,** *From the New World*?
   Was it:
   > a. Borodin?
   > b. Dvorak?
   > c. Eyck?
   > d. Holst?

3. **Who directed the film** *The Battleship Potemkin*?
   Was it:
   > a. David Lean?
   > b. Sergei Eisenstein?
   > c. Ken Russell?
   > d. Luis Bunuel?

4. **Who was the King of Egypt who was forced to abdicate in 1952?**
   Was it:
   > a. Farouk I?
   > b. Faisal?
   > c. Aly Khan?
   > d. Hassan?

5. **Who swam 100 metres in 51.2 seconds at the 1972 Olympics?**
   Was it:
   > a. M. Spitz?
   > b. M. Burton?
   > c. M. Peters?
   > d. M. Belote?

131

6. **What is an orison?**
   Is it:
   - a. A rare fruit?
   - b. A gladiator's helmet?
   - c. A primitive telescope?
   - d. A kind of prayer?

7. **What was the name of Edward I's Queen?**
   Was it:
   - a. Isabella?
   - b. Jane?
   - c. Eleanor?
   - d. Elizabeth?

8. **Who invented the radio valve in 1904?**
   Was it:
   - a. Sir Ambrose Fleming?
   - b. Sir John Vanburgh?
   - c. Sir Roger De Coverly?
   - d. Sir Gerald Nabarro?

9. **What was the nickname of Frederick I, the Holy Roman Emperor who lived from about 1123 to 1190?**
   Was it:
   - a. Charlemagne?
   - b. Frederick the Great?
   - c. Barbarossa?
   - d. Quasimodo?

10. **For what is J. K. Galbraith famous?**
    Is it as:
    - a. A television news reader?
    - b. An open heart surgeon?
    - c. An economist?
    - d. A fighter pilot?

WHAT'S HER NAME?

1. **She was an American author who wrote *Little Women* and lived from 1832 to 1888. What's her name? Is it:**
   - a. Harriet Beecher Stowe?
   - b. Louisa May Alcott?
   - c. Elizabeth Barrett Browning?
   - d. Jane Sarah Dorothea Hoos?

2. **She was a great English actress, who often appeared with Sir Henry Irving and lived from 1848 to 1928. What's her name? Is it:**
   - a. Dame Peggy Ashcroft?
   - b. Dame Edith Evans?
   - c. Dame Marie Tempest?
   - d. Dame Ellen Terry?

3. **She was a Spanish nun famous for her austere life and for her visions. She lived from 1515 to 1582. What's her name? Is it:**
   - a. Saint Joan?
   - b. Saint Teresa?
   - c. Saint Sophia?
   - d. Saint Mary?

4. **She was one of the leading figures of the French Revolution and at her execution in 1793 said, 'O liberty, what crimes are committed in thy name!' What's her name? Is it:**
   - a. Madame Tussaud?
   - b. Madame de Stael?
   - c. Madame de Pompadour?
   - d. Madame Roland?

5. **She lived from 1858 to 1928 and led the movement for votes for women. What's her name?**
   Is it:
   - a. Nancy Astor?
   - b. Dorothy Parker?
   - c. Emmeline Pankhurst?
   - d. Germaine Greer?

6. **She lived from 1820 to 1910 and really created modern nursing. What's her name?**
   Is it:
   - a. Edith Cavell?
   - b. Patricia Nixon?
   - c. Florence Nightingale?
   - d. Rachel Flint?

7. **She was a famous Scottish Jacobite who lived from 1722 to 1790. What's her name?**
   Is it:
   - a. Flora Macdonald?
   - b. Mary, Queen of Scots?
   - c. Kirsty Macleod?
   - d. Glenda Jackson?

8. **She was the most famous of Charles II's mistresses and lived from 1650 to 1687. What's her name?**
   Is it:
   - a. Fanny Burney?
   - b. Lilly Langtry?
   - c. Nell Gwynne?
   - d. Christine Keeler?

9. **She was a Quaker prison reformer who lived from 1780 to 1845. What's her name?**
   Is it:
   - a. Elizabeth Pakenham?
   - b. Sarah Siddons?
   - c. Ann Hathaway?
   - d. Elizabeth Fry?

10. **She was a poet who lived from 1830 to 1894 and wrote *Goblin Market*. What's her name?**
    Is it:
    - a. George Eliot?
    - b. Elizabeth Gaskell?
    - c. Christina Rossetti?
    - d. Emily Brontë?

1. **What is a polemic?**
   Is it:
   - a. A crippling illness?
   - b. A sheepskin coat?
   - c. A controversial discussion?
   - d. A magnetic compass?

2. **Who loved Heloise?**
   Was it:
   - a. Romeo?
   - b. Augustine?
   - c. Abelard?
   - d. Troilus?

3. **When did Napoleon Bonaparte die?**
   Was it in:
   - a. 1812?
   - b. 1815?
   - c. 1821?
   - d. 1840?

4. **Who was the Chilean President killed in 1973?**
   Was it:
   - a. Peron?
   - b. Allende?
   - c. Gomez?
   - d. Castro?

5. **In the television series *Ironside*, who played the title part?**
   Was it:
   - a. Perry Como?
   - b. Perry Mason?
   - c. Patrick Barr?
   - d. Raymond Burr?

6. **Why is Bela Bartok famous?**
   Is it as:
   - a. A German poet?
   - b. A Swiss ski champion?
   - c. An Austrian singer?
   - d. A Hungarian composer?

7. **Who was the English historian and scholar who lived at Jarrow from 673 to 735?**
   Was it:
   - a. Hugh Trevor Roper?
   - b. Antonia Fraser?
   - c. The Venerable Bede?
   - d. William Baxton?

8. **Who wrote the *Pastoral* and *Eroica* symphonies?**
   Was it:
   - a. Beethoven?
   - b. Brahms?
   - c. Bach?
   - d. Bellini?

9. **In 1960 a 56-year-old woman walked from John O'Groats to Land's End. What was her name?**
   Was it:
   - a. Barbara Hepworth?
   - b. Barbara Kelly?
   - c. Barbara Castle?
   - d. Barbara Moore?

10. **Who starred in the film *The Alamo*?**
    Was it:
    - a. Gregory Peck?
    - b. Burt Lancaster?
    - c. Henry Fonda?
    - d. John Wayne?

WHERE'S WHERE?

1. **Where's Aireborough?**
   Is it in:
   - a. England?
   - b. Scotland?
   - c. Australia?
   - d. New Zealand?
2. **Where's Allegheny?**
   Is it in:
   - a. United States of America?
   - b. New Zealand?
   - c. Spain?
   - d. Portugal?
3. **Where's Banagher?**
   Is it in:
   - a. India?
   - b. Pakistan?
   - c. Bangladesh?
   - d. The Republic of Ireland?
4. **Where's Biskra?**
   Is it in:
   - a. Peru?
   - b. Uganda?
   - c. Mexico?
   - d. Algeria?
5. **Where's Creuse?**
   Is it in:
   - a. Greece?
   - b. Switzerland?
   - c. Panama?
   - d. France?

6. Where's Guelph?
Is it in:
      a. Ecuador?
      b. Greenland?
      c. Canada?
      d. Tasmania?

7. Where's Istria?
Is it in:
      a. Turkey?
      b. Israel?
      c. Yugoslavia?
      d. Brazil?

8. Where's Mexborough?
Is it in:
      a. Mexico?
      b. Belgium?
      c. England?
      d. Puerto Rico?

9. Where's Plock?
Is it in:
      a. Germany?
      b. Poland?
      c. South Africa?
      d. Nigeria?

10. Where's Pyongyang?
Is it in:
      a. Vietnam?
      b. Korea?
      c. Cambodia?
      d. Burma?

1. **Where did Billy Bunter go to school?**
   Was it:
   a. St. Jim's?
   b. Rookwood?
   c. Greyfriars?
   d. Carcroft?

2. **In what year was the Anglo-French** *Entente Cordiale*
   established?
   Was it in:
   a. 1805?
   b. 1903?
   c. 1915?
   d. 1967?

3. **The first Earl of Birkenhead was an eminent lawyer and**
   politician. By what name is he best remembered?
   Was it as:
   a. Robert Blake?
   b. Edward Carson?
   c. George Carstairs?
   d. F. E. Smith?

4. **With which kind of entertainment is the name Dan Leno**
   particularly associated?
   Is it with:
   a. Ballet?
   b. Pantomime?
   c. Wrestling?
   d. The cinema?

5. **When was the Colony of Virginia inaugurated at**
   Jamestown?
   Was it in:
   a. 1607?
   b. 1667?
   c. 1707?
   d. 1777?

6. **What is the origin of the *Mayday* distress signal?**
    a. Was it first used on 1 May 1885?
    b. Was it devised by Sir Edward Mayday, the Victorian navigator?
    c. Does it come from the French *m'aidez* meaning 'help me'?
    d. Does it come from the letters M.D. standing for 'Maritime Disaster'?

7. **On a circular compass at how many degrees would you find North East if North is at 0°?**
    Is it at:
    a. 45°?
    b. 90°?
    c. 180°?
    d. 270°?

8. **Who was cast adrift from *The Bounty* by his mutinous crew in 1789?**
    Was it:
    a. Charles Laughton?
    b. James Cook?
    c. William Bligh?
    d. Jasper Hook?

9. **Who was the Queen of the Iceni who fought the Roman Invasion and killed herself in the year 61?**
    Was it:
    a. Cleopatra?
    b. Catherine the Great?
    c. Mary, Queen of Scots?
    d. Boadicea?

10. **What was William Booth's great achievement?**
    Did he:
    a. Fly the Pacific?
    b. Climb the North face of Mount Everest?
    c. Write *Uncle Tom's Cabin*?
    d. Found the Salvation Army?

UNITED STATES PRESIDENTS

1. **When was George Washington President?**
   Was it:
   - a. 1776-1784?
   - b. 1789-1797?
   - c. 1792-1800?
   - d. 1799-1807?

2. **Who was the second American President?**
   Was it:
   - a. Thomas Jefferson?
   - b. James Madison?
   - c. Andrew Jackson?
   - d. John Adams?

3. **Who is the only United States President to have served more than two four-year terms in office?**
   Is it:
   - a. Herbert Hoover?
   - b. Franklin Roosevelt?
   - c. Warren Harding?
   - d. Grover Cleveland?

4. **What was the name of the President who was assassinated in 1901?**
   Was it:
   - a. Abraham Lincoln?
   - b. James Garfield?
   - c. William Harrison?
   - d. William McKinley?

5. **Who was the thirty-fifth President?**
   Was it:
   - a. Woodrow Wilson?
   - b. Harry Truman?
   - c. John Kennedy?
   - d. Gerald Ford?

6. **Who was President from 1837 to 1841?**
   Was it:

   a. Martin Van Buren?
   b. James K. Polk?
   c. Millard Fillmore?
   d. Andrew Jackson?

7. **When Warren Harding died in office in 1923, who succeeded him as President?**
   Was it:

   a. Herbert Hoover?
   b. Calvin Coolidge?
   c. William Taft?
   d. Grover Cleveland?

8. **Who was the first Democrat President of the United States?**
   Was it:

   a. John Quincey Adams?
   b. Andrew Jackson?
   c. Abraham Lincoln?
   d. Ulysses Grant?

9. **Richard Nixon became President in 1969. In what year did he resign?**
   Was it in:

   a. 1971?
   b. 1972?
   c. 1973?
   d. 1974?

10. **Abraham Lincoln was the sixteenth President. Who was the fifteenth?**
    Was it:

    a. James Buchanan?
    b. Andrew Johnson?
    c. Chester Arthur?
    d. Benjamin Harrison?

1. How much does one gallon of pure water weigh?
Is it:

        a. 1 lb?
        b. 10 lb?
        c. 17.26 lb?
        d. 35.89 lb?

2. For what is CO_2 the chemical formula?
Is it:

        a. Water?
        b. Carbon monoxide?
        c. Carbon dioxide?
        d. Nitrous acid?

3. Beatrice Stella Tanner lived from 1865 to 1940 and was an actress celebrated for her beauty and wit. By what name is she best remembered?
Is it:

        a. Mrs. Sarah Siddons?
        b. Dame Marie Tempest?
        c. Mrs. Patrick Campbell?
        d. Dame Margaret Rutherford?

4. In which children's comic did Dan Dare once appear?
Was it:

        a. *Dandy*?
        b. *Beano*?
        c. *The Magnet*?
        d. *The Eagle*?

5. What is Scotland's largest lake?
Is it:

        a. Loch Ness?
        b. Loch Lomond?
        c. Loch Morar?
        d. Loch Awe?

6. **Who was the first man to fly in Great Britain?**
   Was it:
   - a. Samuel Cody?
   - b. Malcolm Campbell?
   - c. Francis Chichester?
   - d. John Collier?

7. **For what is Louis Daguerre famous?**
   Is it as:
   - a. A polar explorer?
   - b. A pioneer of photography?
   - c. A cowboy?
   - d. General de Gaulle's first Prime Minister?

8. **Who succeeded John Masefield as Poet Laureate in 1968?**
   Was it:
   - a. John Betjeman?
   - b. W. H. Auden?
   - c. Cecil Day Lewis?
   - d. Stephen Spender?

9. **Who invented the vacuum flask?**
   Was it:
   - a. Werner Vacuum?
   - b. James Dewar?
   - c. Johnny Walker?
   - d. Walter de la Mare?

10. **In which country could you use a Lira?**
    Is it in:
    - a. Holland?
    - b. Denmark?
    - c. Portugal?
    - d. Italy?

HOME COUNTIES

1. **Since April 1974 (and thanks to the Local Government Act of 1972), Great Britain's counties have been largely rearranged. Some old ones have gone. Some new ones have appeared. How many counties are there in England today?**
    Is it:
    - a. Twenty?
    - b. Thirty-two?
    - c. Forty-six?
    - d. Fifty-eight?

2. **Bristol is the administrative headquarters of which new English county?**
    Is it:
    - a. Somerset?
    - b. Salop?
    - c. Wiltshire?
    - d. Avon?

3. **Yorkshire is now divided into three areas, North Yorkshire, South Yorkshire and West Yorkshire. In acreage it's the largest, but in terms of population North Yorkshire is the smallest of the three. Where is its administrative headquarters?**
    Is it:
    - a. Leeds?
    - b. Barnsley?
    - c. Wakefield?
    - d. Northallerton?

4. **In area which is the largest of the English counties?**
    Is it:
    - a. North Yorkshire?
    - b. Cumbria?
    - c. Tyne and Wear?
    - d. Norfolk?

K

5. **How many counties are there in Wales?**
   Is it:
   - a. Eight?
   - b. Eighteen?
   - c. Twenty-eight?
   - d. Thirty-eight?

6. **Carmarthen is the capital of the largest of the Welsh counties. Which is it?**
   Is it:
   - a. Clwyd?
   - b. Dyfed?
   - c. Gwent?
   - d. Gwynedd?

7. **Cardiff is the capital of Wales. In which county is it situated?**
   Is it:
   - a. Mid Glamorgan?
   - b. South Glamorgan?
   - c. West Glamorgan?
   - d. Powys?

8. **In area, which is Scotland's largest county?**
   Is it:
   - a. Inverness?
   - b. Perth?
   - c. Sutherland?
   - d. Argyll?

9. **Glasgow is the capital of which Scottish county?**
   Is it:
   - a. Lanark?
   - b. Midlothian?
   - c. Kinross?
   - d. Dumfries?

10. **In which of the six counties of Northern Ireland will you find the capital Belfast?**
    Is it:
    - a. Antrim?
    - b. Armagh?
    - c. Fermanagh?
    - d. Londonderry?

ALLSORTS

1. **When does Whit Sunday fall?**
   Is it:
   - a. On the third Sunday after Christmas?
   - b. On the first Sunday in Lent?
   - c. On the Sunday after Easter?
   - d. On the seventh Sunday after Easter?

2. **What is the largest desert in the world?**
   Is it:
   - a. The Sahara?
   - b. The Gobi?
   - c. The Australian?
   - d. The Arabian?

3. **What was the name of the ship in which James Cook sailed round the world between 1768 and 1771?**
   Was it:
   - a. *The Trafalgar*?
   - b. *The Centurion*?
   - c. *The Hispaniola*?
   - d. *The Endeavour*?

4. **Who replaced Sir John French as British commander-in-chief in 1915?**
   Was it:
   - a. Sir Winston Churchill?
   - b. Sir Michael Carver?
   - c. Sir Douglas Haig?
   - d. Sir Hugh Dowding?

5. **What happened to Yuri Gagarin in 1968?**
   Was he:
   - a. The first man to travel through space?
   - b. The first man to walk in space?
   - c. The first Russian to step onto the moon?
   - d. Killed in an air crash?

6. **Who was the English poet who wrote** *The Beggar's Opera*?
   Was it:
     - a. John Gay?
     - b. John Bunyan?
     - c. Lord Byron?
     - d. John Keats?

7. **What war took place in Europe between 1701 and 1713?**
   Was it:
     - a. The Thirty Years War?
     - b. The War of the Spanish Succession?
     - c. The Crimean War?
     - d. The Seven Years War?

8. **When the life of Edward VII was made into a television series, who played the part of Edward?**
   Was it:
     - a. Michael Redgrave?
     - b. John Stride?
     - c. Timothy West?
     - d. James Robertson Justice?

9. **Through which English town is Lady Godiva supposed to have ridden naked in the eleventh century?**
   Was it:
     - a. Banbury?
     - b. Chester?
     - c. Coventry?
     - d. Cirencester?

10. **How many hectares would you expect to find in an acre?**
    Is it:
     - a. None?
     - b. 0.4?
     - c. 4?
     - d. 40?

AMERICAN ENGLISH

1. **What do the British call what the Americans call a billion?**
   Is it:
   - a. A thousand million?
   - b. A billion?
   - c. A trillion?
   - d. A zillion?

2. **What do the British call what the Americans call a bureau?**
   Is it:
   - a. A ballpoint pen?
   - b. A pig's sty?
   - c. A dressing table?
   - d. An insect?

3. **What do the British call what the Americans call a comfort station?**
   Is it:
   - a. A station waiting room?
   - b. A beauty parlour?
   - c. A bus shelter?
   - d. A public lavatory?

4. **What do the British call what the Americans call a faucet?**
   Is it:
   - a. A set of false teeth?
   - b. A doughnut?
   - c. A tap?
   - d. A chest of drawers?

5. **What do the British call what the Americans call gas?**
   Is it:
   - a. Petrol?
   - b. Gas?
   - c. Oil?
   - d. Wind?

6. **What do the British call what the Americans call a line?**
Is it:

      a. A skipping rope?
      b. A wig?
      c. A queue?
      d. A tall story?

7. **What do the British call what the Americans call a night stick?**
Is it:

      a. A torch?
      b. A white walking stick for a blind person?
      c. A shepherd's crook?
      d. A policeman's truncheon?

8. **What do the British call what the Americans call a purse?**
Is it:

      a. A purse?
      b. A wallet?
      c. A handbag?
      d. A briefcase?

9. **What do the British call what the Americans call a realtor?**
Is it:

      a. A realist?
      b. An accountant?
      c. A stockbroker?
      d. An estate agent?

10 **What do the British call what the Americans call a vest?**
Is it:

      a. A vest?
      b. A waistcoat?
      c. A blouse?
      d. A nightshirt?

1. **Who was the Emperor of Ethiopia between 1930 and 1974?**
   Was it:
      a. Haile Selasse I?
      b. Haile Selasse II?
      c. Haile Selasse III?
      d. Haile Dubious?

2. **How many British Thermal Units go to make up one Therm?**
   Is it:
      a. 10?
      b. 100?
      c. 1,000?
      d. 100,000?

3. **Who wrote** *Far From the Madding Crowd*?
   Was it:
      a. Laurie Lee?
      b. Hermann Wouk?
      c. Thomas Hardy?
      d. Rudyard Kipling?

4. **She was the daughter of Henry IV of France and the wife of Charles I of England. What was her name?**
   Was it:
      a. Marie Antoinette?
      b. Henrietta Maria?
      c. Catherine?
      d. Anne?

5. **Who was Prime Minister of New Zealand from 1960 to 1972?**
   Was it:
      a. W. E. Rowling?
      b. Roland Kirk?
      c. Keith Holyoake?
      d. John Dulles?

6. **What is a pontiff?**
   Is it:
       a. An argument?
       b. A life raft?
       c. A chief priest?
       d. A game of cards?
7. **Who wrote** *The Master Builder* **and** *Hedda Gabler*?
   Was it:
       a. Henrik Ibsen?
       b. Georges Feydeau?
       c. Ugo Betti?
       d. August Strindberg?
8. **When did crossword puzzles first start to be popular?**
   Was it around:
       a. 1820?
       b. 1896?
       c. 1923?
       d. 1952?
9. **Horses are measured in hands. How many inches are there to a horse hand?**
   Is it:
       a. Four?
       b. Five?
       c. Six?
       d. Seven?
10. **What do the initials S.O.S. stand for?**
    Is it:
        a. Send Out Someone?
        b. Sink Or Swim?
        c. Save Our Souls?
        d. Salvage Overboard Sinking?

MUSICAL INSTRUMENTS

1. **What's this?**
   Is it:
   - a. A violin?
   - b. A viola?
   - c. A viol?
   - d. A cello? ✓

2. **What's this?**
   Is it:
   - a. An alto saxophone?
   - b. A tenor saxophone?
   - c. A bass saxophone? ✓
   - d. A bassoon?

3. **What's this?**
   Is it:
   - a. A piccolo? ✓
   - b. A flute?
   - c. A recorder?
   - d. A flageolet?

4. **What's this?**
   Is it:
   - a. A French horn?
   - b. A posthorn?
   - c. A tuba?
   - d. A trombone? ✓

5. **What's this?**

   Is it:

   a. A harpsichord? ✓
   b. A spinettina?
   c. A clavichord?
   d. A klavier?

6. **What's this?**

   Is it:

   a. An English horn?
   b. A metal flute?
   c. A penny whistle?
   d. An oboe? ✓

7. **What's this?**

   Is it:

   a. A lute?
   b. A lyre? ✓
   c. A classical guitar?
   d. An electric guitar?

8. **What's this?**

   Is it:

   a. The virginals?
   b. The vibes?
   c. The tympani?
   d. A xylophone? ✓

9. **What's this?**

   Is it:

   a. A trumpet?
   b. A cornet?
   c. A sackbut?
   d. A bugle? ✓

10. **What's this?**

    Is it:

    a. A kettle drum? ✓
    b. A castanet?
    c. A maracas?
    d. A mute?

ALLSORTS

1. **What is a pongo?**
   Is it:
   - a. A large African ape?
   - b. A small Italian waiter?
   - c. A tropical tree?
   - d. A salt-water fish?

2. **In President Kennedy's administration, who was Attorney-General?**
   Was it:
   - a. Elliot Richardson?
   - b. Hubert Humphrey?
   - c. Robert Kennedy?
   - d. Dean Rusk?

3. **What is the name of the Roman poet and Stoic best remembered for his *Satires*?**
   Is it:
   - a. Julian?
   - b. Juvenal?
   - c. Tacitus?
   - d. Virgil?

4. **Who became the President of Kenya in 1964?**
   Was it:
   - a. Jomo Kenyatta?
   - b. Julius Nyere?
   - c. Hastings Banda?
   - d. Ian Smith?

5. **For what is Emanuel Lasker remembered?**
   Is it:
   - a. His riding as a jockey?
   - b. His baritone voice as an opera singer?
   - c. His chess playing as world champion?
   - d. His cooking as principal chef at the Ritz?

6. When was the Airship R101 destroyed on a trip to India?
Was it in:
- a. 1910?
- b. 1920?
- c. 1930?
- d. 1940?

7. When was *Children's Hour* ended by the B.B.C.?
Was it in:
- a. 1953?
- b. 1961?
- c. 1966?
- d. 1976?

8. Who starred in the film *On the Waterfront*?
Was it:
- a. Al Pacino?
- b. Jack Warner?
- c. Marlon Brando?
- d. Robert Shaw?

9. Who wrote the opera *Madame Butterfly*?
Was it:
- a. Mozart?
- b. Rossini?
- c. Vivaldi?
- d. Puccini?

10. What do Americans call the figure 1,000,000,000,000?
Is it:
- a. A million?
- b. A billion?
- c. A trillion?
- d. A quadrillion?

ASTRONOMY

1. **Bungula is the name of the star nearest the planet Earth. How far away is it?**
   Is it:
   - a. 25,000,000 miles away?
   - b. 25,000,000,000 miles away?
   - c. 25,000,000,000,000 miles away?
   - d. 25,000,000,000,000,000 miles away?

2. **Roughly how many miles are there to a light-year?**
   Are there:
   - a. 6,000,000,000,000,000 miles?
   - b. 6,000,000,000,000 miles?
   - c. 6,000,000,000 miles?
   - d. 6,000,000 miles?

3. **In Great Britain on a cloudless night how many stars are visible to the naked eye?**
   Is it:
   - a. Between 200 and 300?
   - b. Between 2,000 and 3,000?
   - c. Between 20,000 and 30,000?
   - d. Between 200,000 and 300,000?

4. **What is the name of the brightest star?**
   Is it:
   - a. Sirius?
   - b. Capella?
   - c. Pollux?
   - d. Canopus?

5. **What is the diameter of the sun?**
   Is it:
   - a. 864 miles?
   - b. 8,640 miles?
   - c. 86,400 miles?
   - d. 864,000 miles?

6. **How long does the planet Earth take to revolve around the sun?**
   Is it:
   - a. 364 days?
   - b. 365 days?
   - c. 365¼ days?
   - d 365⅓ days?
7. **How long does the planet Pluto take to revolve around the sun?**
   Is it:
   - a. 248.43 days?
   - b. 248.43 weeks?
   - c. 248.43 months?
   - d. 248.43 years?
8. **Which of the planets is nearest to the sun?**
   Is it:
   - a. Earth?
   - b. Venus?
   - c. Mercury?
   - d. Mars?
9. **How long does the moon take to revolve around the Earth?**
   Is it:
   - a. 27 days 7 hours 43 minutes 11 seconds?
   - b. 28 days 9 hours 10 minutes 51 seconds?
   - c. 29 days 12 hours 30 minutes 30 seconds?
   - d. 30 days exactly?
10. **Ursa Major is the scientific name for one of the constellations of stars. What is its common English name?**
    Is it:
    - a. The Northern Crown?
    - b. The Chained Lady?
    - c. The Milky Way?
    - d. The Great Bear?

1. **For what achievement is the £5,000 Booker Prize awarded each year?**
   Is it for:
       a. An outstanding contribution to science?
       b. An outstanding piece of architecture?
       c. An outstanding performance in the theatre?
       d. An outstanding novel?

2. **Who was the Squash Rackets Open Champion in 1966, 1967, 1969, 1970, 1971 and 1972?**
   Was it:
       a. Qamar Zaman?
       b. Abu Taleb?
       c. Jonah Barrington?
       d. Azam Khan?

3. **How many grains go into a scruple?**
   Is it:
       a. Ten?
       b. Twenty?
       c. Thirty?
       d. One hundred?

4. **Who founded antiseptic surgery?**
   Was it:
       a. Joseph Lister?
       b. Thomas Lipton?
       c. Franz Liszt?
       d. Walter Lippmann?

5. **When did the first Mickey Mouse cartoon film appear?**
   Was it in:
       a. 1928?
       b. 1934?
       c. 1939?
       d. 1951?

6. **What does an oreologist study?**
   Is it:
   a. Ears?
   b. Mountains?
   c. Kidneys?
   d. Ancient manuscripts?
7. **Who starred in the films** *Queen Christina* **and** *Ninotchka*?
   Was it:
   a. Marlene Dietrich?
   b. Mae West?
   c. Greta Garbo?
   d. Vivien Leigh?
8. **When was William Shakespeare born?**
   Was it in:
   a. 1564?
   b. 1600?
   c. 1624?
   d. 1668?
9. **Who wrote the** *Kettledrum* **Symphony?**
   Was it:
   a. Beethoven?
   b. Haydn?
   c. Brahms?
   d. Bach?
10. **Whose mistress was Nell Gwynne?**
    Was it:
    a. Charles I?
    b. Charles II?
    c. James I?
    d. James II?

SEA TALK

1. **In nautical terms, what does 'bilge' mean?**
   Is it:
   a. The broadest part of a ship's bottom?
   b. The rim of a hatchway?
   c. The hatch through which rubbish is placed?
   d. A slang expression meaning 'the captain's orders'?

2. **In nautical terms, what is a 'cable'?**
   Is it:
   a. The wire to which the anchor is attached?
   b. A rope ladder leading down to a cabin?
   c. A sea measure of 100 fathoms?
   d. A light rowing boat?

3. **In nautical terms, where is 'starboard'?**
   Is it:
   a. The right side of the ship looking forward?
   b. The left side of the ship looking forward?
   c. The front of the ship?
   d. The rear of the ship?

4. **In nautical terms, what is a 'grapnel'?**
   Is it:
   a. A type of compass?
   b. A type of rope?
   c. A type of anchor?
   d. A type of sail?

5. **In nautical terms, what is a 'binnacle'?**
   Is it:
   a. A case to house a compass?
   b. A spar projecting from a bow?
   c. A petty officer in charge of part of the crew?
   d. The cooking quarters on a ship?

L

6. **In nautical terms, what is the meaning of 'abaft'?**
Is it:

   a. Behind?
   b. Ahead?
   c. To the right?
   d. To the left?

7. **In nautical terms, what are 'scuppers'?**
Are they:

   a. The rations given to mutineers when they have been arrested on board ship?
   b. The safety rafts that have to be carried on all ocean-going liners?
   c. The ropes that support the main mast of a ship?
   d. The holes in a ship's sides used to drain water from the decks?

8. **In nautical terms, when is 'the night watch'?**
Is it:

   a. From 4.00 pm to 8.00 pm?
   b. From 6.00 pm to 10.00 pm?
   c. From 10.00 pm to 2.00 am?
   d. From midnight to 4.00 am?

9. **In nautical terms, what is a 'hawser'?**
Is it:

   a. A type of navigational instrument?
   b. A type of hatchway?
   c. A type of ship's wheel?
   d. A type of rope?

10. **How deep is a fathom?**
Is it:

   a. 3 feet?
   b. 6 feet?
   c. 10 feet?
   d. 30 feet?

1. **Herod the Great was Governor of Galilee under the Romans, but he became a king in his own right in 31 BC. Where was his kingdom?**
   Was it in:
   - a. Judea?
   - b. Gaza?
   - c. Sinai?
   - d. Aqaba?

2. **When did Oliver Cromwell die?**
   Was it in:
   - a. 1641?
   - b. 1658?
   - c. 1672?
   - d. 1681?

3. **What London Theatre had the motto 'We Never Closed' — until it did, in 1964?**
   Was it:
   - a. The Ambassadors?
   - b. The Winter Gardens?
   - c. The Lyceum?
   - d. The Windmill?

4. **What famous family of writers lived at Haworth, near Keighley, in Yorkshire?**
   Was it:
   - a. The Scotts?
   - b. The Brownings?
   - c. The Wordsworths?
   - d. The Brontës?

5. **What is the highest structure in the United Kingdom?**
Is it:
      a. The Post Office Tower in London?
      b. The I.B.A. Television Mast at Emley Moor in Yorkshire?
      c. The I.B.A. Television Mast at Belmont in Lincolnshire?
      d. St. Paul's Cathedral in London?

6. **How far can you see at a height of 20,000 feet?**
Can you see:
      a. Five miles?
      b. 95 miles?
      c. 186 miles?
      d. 3,651 miles?

7. **What was the pseudonym of Eric Arthur Blair?**
Was it:
      a. Edgar Wallace?
      b. George Orwell?
      c. Hammond Innes?
      d. John Braine?

8. **What number do the Roman numerals MCMLXXVII represent?**
Is it:
      a. 1066?
      b. 1977?
      c. 101566233?
      d. 343566211?

9. **When did the half-crown cease to be legal tender?**
Was it in:
      a. 1914?
      b. 1965?
      c. 1970?
      d. 1973?

10. **On what day in 1789 did the Storming of the Bastille take place?**
Was it on:
      a. 4 June?
      b. 4 July?
      c. 14 July?
      d. 6 December?

INTERNATIONAL LETTERS

1. **When you see the letter A on a car, what country does the car come from?**
   Is it:
   - a. Austria?
   - b. Australia?
   - c. Albania?
   - d. Hong Kong?

2. **When you see the letters YV on a car, what country does the car come from?**
   Is it:
   - a. Yugoslavia?
   - b. The Yemen?
   - c. Sicily?
   - d. Venezuela?

3. **When you see the letter C on a car, what country does the car come from?**
   Is it:
   - a. Canada?
   - b. Chile?
   - c. Cuba?
   - d. Switzerland?

4. **When you see the letters MC on a car, what country does the car come from?**
   Is it:
   - a. Morocco?
   - b. Mexico?
   - c. Monaco?
   - d. The Netherlands?

5. **When you see the letter E on a car, what country does the car come from?**
   Is it:
   - a. Egypt?
   - b. Ecuador?
   - c. England?
   - d. Spain?

6. **When you see the letters FL on a car, what country does the car come from?**
   Is it:
   - a. Formosa?
   - b. The Faroe Islands?
   - c. The Falkland Islands?
   - d. Liechtenstein?

7. **When you see the letters RA on a car, what country does the car come from?**
   Is it:
   - a. Rhodesia?
   - b. Rumania?
   - c. The Soviet Union?
   - d. Argentina?

8. **When you see the letter V on a car, what country does the car come from?**
   Is it:
   - a. Venezuela?
   - b. The Virgin Islands?
   - c. The Vatican City?
   - d. Thailand?

9. **When you see the letter L on a car, what country does the car come from?**
   Is it:
   - a. Liberia?
   - b. Laos?
   - c. Luxembourg?
   - d. Lithuania?

10. **When you see the letters ZA on a car, what country does the car come from?**
    Is it:
    - a. Zambia?
    - b. Zaire?
    - c. Zanzibar?
    - d. South Africa?

1. **When Napoleon abdicated in 1814, who became king of France?**
   Was it:
   - a. Napoleon II?
   - b. Napoleon III?
   - c. Louis XVI?
   - d. Louis XVIII?

2. **If £1 was worth 100p in 1914, how much do you think £1 was worth in 1974?**
   Was it:
   - a. 83p?
   - b. 50p?
   - c. 37p?
   - d. 10p?

3. **For what will David Wilkie be remembered?**
   Is it:
   - a. His tapestries?
   - b. His design for Coventry Cathedral?
   - c. His invention of the telephone?
   - d. His record-breaking swimming?

4. **What did Ludwig Mies Van der Rohe and Richard Neutra have in common?**
   Were they both:
   - a. Music hall comedians?
   - b. Prize-winning marine biologists?
   - c. Composers of light operas?
   - d. Famous architects?

5. **What important world leader died on 6 March 1953?**
   Was it:
   - a. General de Gaulle?
   - b. Sir Winston Churchill?
   - c. Marshal Stalin?
   - d. General Franco?

6. **What was the name of the dog that starred in** *The Magic Roundabout*?
   Was it:
   - a. Lassie?
   - b. Rin Tin Tin?
   - c. Dougal?
   - d. Nana?

7. **Who wrote** *Kipps*?
   Was it:
   - a. Frederick Marryat?
   - b. Matthew Arnold?
   - c. W. H. Davies?
   - d. H. G. Wells?

8. **When** *Peter Pan* **was turned into a television musical, who played Peter and who played Captain Hook?**
   Was it:
   - a. Lulu and Ron Moody?
   - b. Maggie Smith and Dave Allen?
   - c. Hayley Mills and Eric Porter?
   - d. Mia Farrow and Danny Kaye?

9. **What was a speakeasy?**
   Was it:
   - a. An early form of telephone?
   - b. A jaw rest?
   - c. An illegal drinking place?
   - d. An electric tram?

10. **By what English name is the constellation Andromeda known?**
    Is it:
    - a. The Ram?
    - b. The Giant Hunter?
    - c. The Southern Crown?
    - d. The Chained Lady?

SPORT

1. **As a light-heavyweight he won a gold medal in the 1960 Olympic Games. What's his name?**
    Is it:
    - a. Sonny Liston?
    - b. Floyd Paterson?
    - c. Ingemar Johansson?
    - d. Cassius Clay?

2. **Born in 1920 in Bury, Lancashire, what is the sport of Reg Harris, OBE?**
    Is it:
    - a. Archery?
    - b. Long-distance running?
    - c. Swimming?
    - d. Cycling?

3. **What happened to Gary Player in 1959, 1968 and 1974?**
    Did he:
    - a. Win the British Open?
    - b. Win the British Open and the U.S. Open?
    - c. Win the American Masters?
    - d. Win the British Open, the U.S. Open, the French Open *and* the American Masters?

4. **Who won the Admiral's Cup Yacht Race in 1973?**
    Was it:
    - a. United States?
    - b. Great Britain?
    - c. Australia?
    - d. West Germany?

5. **To win both the Swaythling Cup and the Corbillon Cup, what sport would you need to play?**
    - a. Volley Ball?
    - b. Table Tennis?
    - c. Snooker
    - d. Squash Rackets?

6. **In 1974 Warrington won and in 1975 Widnes won. What's the sport and what's the competition? Is it:**
   - a. The Netball Inter-county Championship?
   - b. The Rugby League Challenge Cup?
   - c. The Rugby Union County Championship?
   - d. The Water Polo Challenge Cup?
7. **Phil Read has fifty Grand Prix wins to his credit and seven World Championships. What's his sport?**
   - a. Cycling?
   - b. Motor cycling?
   - c. Motor racing?
   - d. Horse racing?
8. **Who was the World Heavyweight Boxing Champion of the World from 1937 to 1949? Was it:**
   - a. Joe Louis?
   - b. Rocky Marciano?
   - c. Jack Dempsey?
   - d. Ezzard Charles?
9. **Apart from Australia and the United States, what one country has won the Davis Cup at Lawn Tennis most often since 1950? Is it:**
   - a. Great Britain?
   - b. France?
   - c. New Zealand?
   - d. South Africa?
10. **He started his career as a professional footballer playing for Ajax of Amsterdam but left them for CF de Barcelona in 1973. What's his name? Is it:**
    - a. Danny Blanchflower?
    - b. Kevin Keegan?
    - c. Pele?
    - d. Johan Cruyff?

1. **How was Lev Davidovich Bronstein better known?**
    Was it as:
    > a. Lenin?
    > b. Stalin?
    > c. Trotsky?
    > d. Bulganin?

2. **Who wrote** *The Warden* **and** *Barchester Towers*?
    Was it:
    > a. Anthony Powell?
    > b. Anthony Trollope?
    > c. Eric Ambler?
    > d. John Le Carré?

3. **Who discovered Tasmania?**
    Was it:
    > a. Abel Tasman?
    > b. Joshua Tasmania?
    > c. James Cook?
    > d. John Cabot?

4. **What is the speed of light?**
    Is it:
    > a. 1 mile per second?
    > b. 14 miles per second?
    > c. 29 miles per second?
    > d. 186,000 miles per second?

5. **What journals did Sir Richard Steel found?**
    Was it:
    > a. *The Tatler?*
    > b. *The Spectator?*
    > c. *The Guardian?*
    > d. *Chick's Own?*

6. **Who produced and starred in the film** *Shampoo*?
   Was it:
   - a. Richard Burton?
   - b. Richard Benjamin?
   - c. Warren Beatty?
   - d. Dean Martin?

7. **Who wrote the play** *The Rivals*?
   Was it:
   - a. Sir John Vanbrugh?
   - b. Oliver Goldsmith?
   - c. R. B. Sheridan?
   - d. G. B. Shaw?

8. **What is Telstar?**
   Is it:
   - a. The name of a character in the comic *Beezer*?
   - b. The name of the first dog to fly in space?
   - c. The name of a radar system developed during the Second World War?
   - d. The name of the first television satellite launched by the United States?

9. **How many degrees Fahrenheit are there in 100°Centigrade?**
   Is it:
   - a. 12°?
   - b. 36°?
   - c. 60°?
   - d. 212°?

10. **In what year was Charles II crowned King of Scotland at Scone?**
    Was it in:
    - a. 1640?
    - b. 1651?
    - c. 1666?
    - d. 1675?

ART AND ARTISTS

1. **What famous painting was completed by Leonardo da Vinci in 1500?**
   Was it:
   - a. *The Laughing Cavalier?*
   - b. *The Mona Lisa?*
   - c. *The Last Judgement?*
   - d. *The Bunch of Grapes?*

2. **He was a painter and architect who lived from 1483 to 1520 and was called Raffaello Sanzio. By what name is he now better known?**
   Is it:
   - a. Michelangelo?
   - b. Donatello?
   - c. Giotto?
   - d. Raphael?

3. **In what sort of painting did the English artists Nicholas Hillyarde (1547-1619) and Samuel Cooper (1609-72) specialise?**
   Did they specialise in:
   - a. Abstract art?
   - b. Nudes?
   - c. Landscapes?
   - d. Miniatures?

4. **Domenicos Theotocopoulos was a visionary Spaniard who lived from 1541 to 1614. By what name is he better known?**
   Is it:
   - a. El Greco?
   - b. Goya?
   - c. Velasquez?
   - d. Rubens?

5. What kind of artist was Inigo Jones?
Was he:

    a. A specialist in water colours?
    b. A sculptor?
    c. An architect?
    d. A dress designer?

6. Between 1508 and 1512 he painted the ceiling of the Sistine Chapel at Saint Peter's in Rome. What was his name?
Was it:

    a. Sandro Botticelli?
    b. Michelangelo Buonarotti?
    c. Antonio Correggio?
    d. Michelangelo da Caravaggio?

7. Who was the American pioneer of 'action painting' who lived from 1912 to 1956?
Was it:

    a. Mark Rothko?
    b. Paul Klee?
    c. Jackson Pollock?
    d. G. F. Watts?

8. Benvenuto Cellini lived from 1500 to 1571. For what is he best remembered?
Is it:

    a. For his oil paintings?
    b. For his tapestries?
    c. For his mosaics?
    d. For his sculptures?

9. In 1865 who painted *Le Déjeuner sur l'Herbe*?
Was it:

    a. Monet?
    b. Manet?
    c. Dégas?
    d. Renoir?

10. What is the name of the great Spanish painter who painted the first Duke of Wellington?
Was it:

    a. Salvador Dali?
    b. Francesco Goya?
    c. Pablo Picasso?
    d. Paolo Uccello?

1. **On television in the early 1970s who was known as the 'Galloping Gourmet'?**
   Was it:
   > a. Fanny Cradock?
   > b. Julia Childs?
   > c. Zena Skinner?
   > d. Graham Kerr?

2. **What was the name of the influential monk who was at the court of Tsar Nicholas II of Russia?**
   Was it:
   > a. Dracula?
   > b. Hopalong Cassidy?
   > c. Rasputin?
   > d. Grigori?

3. **What did Sir Isaac Pitman invent?**
   Was it:
   > a. The typewriter?
   > b. A form of shorthand writing?
   > c. The propelling pencil?
   > d. The fountain pen?

4. **Who was the great Polish pianist and prime minister who lived from 1860 to 1941?**
   Was it:
   > a. Paganini?
   > b. Pachmann?
   > c. Paderewski?
   > d. Palestrina?

5. **Who wrote** *Apologia Pro Vita Sua*?
   Was it:
   > a. Thomas Campion?
   > b. John Henry Newman?
   > c. Trevor Huddleston?
   > d. Pope John XXIII?

6. **For what is Sir Osbert Lancaster famous?**
   Is it for:
     a. His design of the Lancaster bomber?
     b. His term as Home Secretary under Sir Winston Churchill?
     c. His pocket cartoons?
     d. His work as an astronomer?
7. **What was the name of the short-story writer who was born in New Zealand in 1890 and who died in 1923?**
   Was it:
     a. A. Asimov?
     b. Thomas Mann?
     c. Katherine Mansfield?
     d. John Middleton Murry?
8. **What are cumulus, stratus, nimbostratus and altostratus?**
   Are they:
     a. Constellations of stars?
     b. Species of animal?
     c. Varieties of flower?
     d. Types of cloud formation?
9. **What is the capital of Liechtenstein?**
   Is it:
     a. Monaco?
     b. Luxembourg?
     c. Vaduz?
     d. Valais?
10. **Who became King of the French in 771?**
    Was it:
      a. Louis X?
      b. François I?
      c. Charles V?
      d. Charlemagne?

GET KNOTTED

1. **This knot is used for tying two ropes together. What's it called?**
   Is it:
   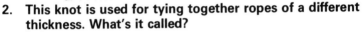
   - a. A reef knot?
   - b. A sheet bend?
   - c. A clove hitch?
   - d. A wall knot?

2. **This knot is used for tying together ropes of a different thickness. What's it called?**
   Is it:
   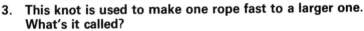
   - a. A reef knot?
   - b. A sheet bend?
   - c. A clove hitch?
   - d. A wall knot?

3. **This knot is used to make one rope fast to a larger one. What's it called?**
   Is it:

   - a. A bowline?
   - b. A sheepshank?
   - c. A clove hitch?
   - d. A figure of eight?

4. **This knot is used for temporarily shortening a rope. What's it called?**
   Is it:

   - a. A bowline?
   - b. A sheepshank?
   - c. A clove hitch?
   - d. A figure of eight?

5. **This knot is used to tie ropes to poles. What's it called?**
   Is it:
   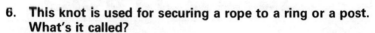
   a. A figure of eight?
   b. A half-hitch?
   c. A timber hitch?
   d. A wall knot?

6. **This knot is used for securing a rope to a ring or a post. What's it called?**
   Is it:
   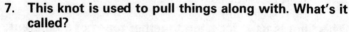
   a. A half-hitch?
   b. A timber hitch?
   c. A round turn and two half-hitches?
   d. A wall knot?

7. **This knot is used to pull things along with. What's it called?**
   Is it:
   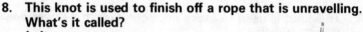
   a. A half-hitch?
   b. A timber hitch?
   c. A round turn and two half-hitches?
   d. A sheepshank?

8. **This knot is used to finish off a rope that is unravelling. What's it called?**
   Is it:
   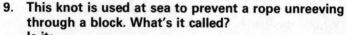
   a. A sheepshank?
   b. A wall knot?
   c. A timber hitch?
   d. A double sheet bend?

9. **This knot is used at sea to prevent a rope unreeving through a block. What's it called?**
   Is it:
   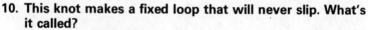
   a. A sheepshank?
   b. A double sheet bend?
   c. A bowline?
   d. A figure of eight?

10. **This knot makes a fixed loop that will never slip. What's it called?**
    Is it:
    a. A double sheet bend?

    b. A bowline?
    c. A figure of eight?
    d. A reef knot?

ALLSORTS

1. **For what is Thomas Malthus famous?**
   Is it for:
   - a. Discovering Australia?
   - b. Building the Tay Bridge?
   - c. Writing *The Principle of Population*?
   - d. Inventing colour television?

2. **How many cubic inches will you find in a cubic foot?**
   Is it:
   - a. 1,728?
   - b. 144?
   - c. 12?
   - d. 3?

3. **What did Friedrich Sertürner discover in 1805?**
   Was it:
   - a. Radium?
   - b. Morphine?
   - c. Fluoride?
   - d. Hydrogen?

4. **What is Great Britain's highest peak?**
   Is it:
   - a. Ben Nevis?
   - b. Cairngorm?
   - c. Snowdon?
   - d. Scafell?

5. **When is Commonwealth Day?**
   is it:
   - a. 1 January?
   - b. 24 May?
   - c. 2 June?
   - d. 21 October?

6. **Who wrote a famous poem about Kubla Khan, the first Mongol Emperor of China?**
   Was it:
   - a. Keats?
   - b. Coleridge?
   - c. Shelley?
   - d. Swinburne?

7. **In what year is it now reckoned that Jesus was probably born?**
   Was it in:
   - a. 4 BC?
   - b. AD 1?
   - c. AD 4?
   - d. AD 30?

8. **Who was the English judge who held the notorious 'bloody assize'?**
   Was it:
   - a. Lord Denning?
   - b. Lord Parker?
   - c. Lord Jeffreys?
   - d. Lord Salmon?

9. **Who wrote *Three Men in a Boat*?**
   Was it:
   - a. Gore Vidal?
   - b. Bennett Cerf?
   - c. Jerome K. Jerome?
   - d. Saki?

10. **What is the religion with most members?**
    Is it:
    - a. Christianity?
    - b. Islam?
    - c. Judaism?
    - d. Buddhism?

1. **It was once called British Honduras. What's it called today?**
   Is it:
   - a. New Guinea?
   - b. Honduras?
   - c. Bélize?
   - d. Gabon?

2. **It was once called Cambodia. What's it called today?**
   Is it:
   - a. Ho Republic?
   - b. Khmer Republic?
   - c. People's Republic of Cambodia?
   - d. Cam Republic?

3. **It was once called Lake Edward. What's it called today?**
   Is it:
   - a. Lake Victoria?
   - b. Lake Uganda?
   - c. Lake Callaghan?
   - d. Lake Idi Amin Dada?

4. **It was once called Cape Kennedy. What's it called today?**
   Is it:
   - a. Cape John F. Kennedy?
   - b. Cape Cod?
   - c. Cape Canaveral?
   - d. Cape Carter?

5. **It was once called the Congo River. What's it called today?**
   Is it:
   - a. River Brazzaville?
   - b. River Kinshasa?
   - c. River Lumumba?
   - d. River Zaire?

6. **It was once called Algiers. What's it called today?**
   Is it:
   a. El Djezair?
   b. Alhambra?
   c. Bouzarea?
   d. Numidia?
7. **It was once called the United Arab Republic. What's it called today?**
   Is it:
   a. Nasserland?
   b. The Federated Arab States?
   c. Arabia?
   d. The Arab Republic of Egypt?
8. **It was once called Casablanca. What's it called today?**
   Is it:
   a. Rabat?
   b. Agadir?
   c. El-Dar-el-Beida?
   d. Djebel Toubkai?
9. **It was once called Ceylon. What's it called today?**
   Is it:
   a. Srinagar?
   b. Sri Lanka?
   c. Colombo?
   d. Nuwara Eliya?
10. **It was once called Muscat and Oman. What's it called today?**
    Is it:
    a. The Republic of Muscat?
    b. Muscady?
    c. The Sultanate of Oman?
    d. Oman Khayam?

1. Who or what was Tinkerbell?
Was it:
  a. The boat in which Sir Francis Chichester sailed around the world?
  b. The horse that won the 1976 Grand National?
  c. The nickname of the first manned space ship?
  d. The name of Peter Pan's fairy?

2. Who drew *The Rake's Progress*?
Was it:
  a. William Hogarth?
  b. E. H. Shepherd?
  c. John Ruskin?
  d. Augustus John?

3. Who was the last Saxon king of England?
Was it:
  a. Harold I?
  b. Harold II?
  c. William I?
  d. William II?

4. Who invented 'one-upmanship'?
Was it:
  a. Nancy Spain?
  b. Paul Jennings?
  c. Stephen Potter?
  d. Damon Runyan?

5. Who was the English metaphysical poet who was also Dean of St. Paul's?
Was it:
  a. Andrew Marvell?
  b. Martin Sullivan?
  c. John Donne?
  d. Jonathan Swift?

183

6. **Who invented the Pobble who had no toes?**
   Was it:
     a. Lewis Carroll?
     b. G. K. Chesterton?
     c. Ogden Nash?
     d. Edward Lear?

7. **Which famous theatre in London was built by Richard D'Oyly Carte?**
   Was it:
     a. The Globe?
     b. The Savoy?
     c. The Vaudeville?
     d. The Theatre Royal, Haymarket?

8. **Who starred in the films** *Shoulder Arms* **and** *The Kid*?
   Was it:
     a. Elsa Lanchester?
     b. Harold Lloyd?
     c. Charlie Chaplin?
     d. Buster Keaton?

9. **Who wrote** *The Canterbury Tales*?
   Was it:
     a. Nevill Coghill?
     b. Piers Plowman?
     c. Geoffrey Chaucer?
     d. Thomas Kyd?

10. **What did Leo H. Baekeland invent in 1907?**
    Was it:
     a. Bakelite?
     b. Plastic?
     c. Foam rubber?
     d. Perspex?

NOBEL PRIZEWINNERS

1. **Who won the Nobel Prize for Literature in 1970?**
   Was it:
   - a. Jean-Paul Sartre?
   - b. Alexander Solzhenitsyn?
   - c. Patrick White?
   - d. Heinrich Boll?

2. **Who shared the Nobel Peace Prize with Henry Kissinger in 1973?**
   Was it:
   - a. Richard Nixon?
   - b. Willy Brandt?
   - c. Le Duc Tho?
   - d. Martin Luther King?

3. **Which British female scientist won the Nobel Prize for Chemistry in 1964?**
   Was it:
   - a. Jane Osborn?
   - b. Mary Hagger?
   - c. Dorothy Hodgkin?
   - d. Shirley Wilkes?

4. **Who was the first Briton to win the Nobel Prize for Literature?**
   Was it:
   - a. Arthur Conan Doyle?
   - b. Rudyard Kipling?
   - c. E. M. Forster?
   - d. George Bernard Shaw?

5. **A father and son were joint winners of the Nobel Prize for Physics in 1915. What was their surname?**
   Was it:
   - a. Compton?
   - b. Richardson?
   - c. Stark?
   - d. Bragg?

6. **For what was Lord Todd awarded a Nobel Prize in 1957? Was it for:**
    - a. Peace?
    - b. Physics?
    - c. Chemistry?
    - d. Physiology and Medicine?
7. **What organisation won the Nobel Peace Prize in 1965? Was it:**
    - a. UNICEF?
    - b. The International Labour Organisation?
    - c. The Boy Scout Movement?
    - d. The International Red Cross?
8. **Who has won both Nobel Peace Prize and the Nobel Prize for Chemistry? Was it:**
    - a. Cyril Hinshelwood?
    - b. Linus Pauling?
    - c. Marie Curie?
    - d. Peter Medawar?
9. **Who was the last Irishman to win a Nobel Prize? Was it:**
    - a. Samuel Beckett for Literature?
    - b. Timothy Kelly for Physics?
    - c. Sean MacBride for Peace?
    - d. Brendan Behan for Literature?
10. **A new Nobel Prize was introduced in 1969. What discipline does it cover? Is it:**
    - a. Economic Sciences?
    - b. Ecology?
    - c. Psychology?
    - d. Biology?

1. **What did the American Charles Towney discover in 1960?**
   Was it:
      a. The laser beam?
      b. Teflon?
      c. How to put stripes into toothpaste?
      d. A cure for asthma?

2. **Of what trade is St. Crispin traditionally the patron saint?**
   Is it:
      a. Baking?
      b. Shoemaking?
      c. Pawnbroking?
      d. Carpentry?

3. **What is a poniard?**
   Is it:
      a. A scarf?
      b. A deadly poison?
      c. A cross between a donkey and a mule?
      d. A dagger?

4. **Who wrote the poem *John Gilpin*?**
   Was it:
      a. William Cowper?
      b. Lord Tennyson?
      c. Lord Byron?
      d. Philip Larkin?

5. **For what was Sir Geoffrey de Havilland famous?**
   Was it for:
      a. Pioneering organ transplants?
      b. Designing the Royal Albert Hall?
      c. Designing aircraft?
      d. Pioneering the use of anaesthetics?

6. **Who was the father of David II, King of Scotland?**
   Was it:
         a. Henry I of England?
         b. David of Scotland?
         c. Macbeth?
         d. Robert Bruce?

7. **Who founded the Church of Christ Scientist?**
   Was it:
         a. Mary Whitehouse?
         b. Mary Tyler Moore?
         c. Mary Baker Eddy?
         d. Milly Molly Mandy?

8. **Who was the Greek dramatist who lived from 480 to 406 BC and wrote** Medea, Orestes **and eighty other plays?**
   Was it:
         a. Euripides?
         b. Plautus?
         c. Sophocles?
         d. Damocles?

9. **For what was Jacob Epstein famous?**
   Was it:
         a. For his piano playing?
         b. For being World Heavyweight Boxing Champion?
         c. For his sculpture?
         d. For writing Black Sambo?

10. **When was the Argentinian revolutionary Che Guevara killed?**
   Was it in:
         a. 1935?
         b. 1956?
         c. 1967?
         d. 1972?

FOREIGN PHRASES

1. **What is a** *nom de plume*?
   Is it:
   - a. A French wine?
   - b. A pen name?
   - c. An infinite number?
   - d. A peacock's feather?

2. **What does** *al fresco* **mean?**
   Is it:
   - a. Ice cold?
   - b. Afternoon?
   - c. Never say die?
   - d. In the open air?

3. **What is a** *bonne bouche*?
   Is it:
   - a. A big mouth?
   - b. A vain person?
   - c. A tasty morsel?
   - d. A hot shower?

4. **What does** *ich dien* **mean?**
   Is it:
   - a. I serve?
   - b. I eat?
   - c. I itch?
   - d. I die?

5. **What does répondez, s'il vous plaît mean?**
   Is it:
   - a. Do not break the crockery?
   - b. Do not answer back: it's rude?
   - c. A stitch in time saves nine?
   - d. Reply, please?

6. **What does** *tout de suite* **mean?**
   Is it:
   - a. On the following day?
   - b. Immediately?
   - c. In one mouthful?
   - d. A three-piece suit?

7. **What does** *basta!* **mean?**
   Is it:
   - a. Open up!?
   - b. More spaghetti please!?
   - c. You swine!?
   - d. Enough!?

8. **What does** *caput* **mean?**
   Is it:
   - a. Completely done for?
   - b. Keep your hair on!?
   - c. If the cap fits, wear it?
   - d. Lights out!?

9. **What does** *entre nous* **mean?**
   Is it:
   - a. Enter now?
   - b. Between ourselves?
   - c. Keep your wits about you?
   - d. Time waits for no man?

10. **What is a** *faux pas*?
    Is it:
    - a. A false step?
    - b. A faun father?
    - c. A white lie?
    - d. A matter of honour?

1. **What is roup?**
   Is it:
   - a. A kind of onion soup?
   - b. A disease that poultry get?
   - c. A type of whooping cough?
   - d. An extinct volcano's lava?

2. **Who wrote *The Diary of a Nobody*?**
   Was it:
   - a. George and Weedon Grossmith?
   - b. Elsie and Doris Waters?
   - c. Harold Nicolson?
   - d. Chips Channon?

3. **Who was the Pope who introduced the Gregorian calendar that we use to this day?**
   Was it:
   - a. Gregory I?
   - b. Gregory III?
   - c. Gregory X?
   - d. Gregory XIII?

4. **How many runs did W. G. Grace score in May 1895?**
   Was it:
   - a. 100?
   - b. 342?
   - c. 769?
   - d. 1,000?

5. **What was the nickname of General Thomas Jackson, one of the Southern leaders in the American Civil War?**
   Was it:
   - a. Hawkeye?
   - b. Southern Tom?
   - c. Stonewall?
   - d. Uncle Sam?

6. **Who is the British comedian associated with Odd Odes?**
   Is it:
   - a. Mike Yarwood?
   - b. Eric Morecambe?
   - c. Arthur Askey?
   - d. Cyril Fletcher?

7. **Who wrote *The Go-Between*?**
   Was it:
   - a. Susan Hill?
   - b. L. P. Hartley?
   - c. William Golding?
   - d. William Faulkner?

8. **What have Sirocco and Zonda in common?**
   Are they both:
   - a. The names of Julius Caesar's eldest daughters?
   - b. The names of blood deficiencies?
   - c. The names of winds?
   - d. The names of New York nightclubs?

9. **For which English king was Windsor Castle built?**
   Was it for:
   - a. Henry III?
   - b. Henry VIII?
   - c. George IV?
   - d. George VI?

10. **What is the name of the Cardinal Archbishop of Westminster?**
    Is it:
    - a. John Heenan?
    - b. Donald Coggan?
    - c. Basil Hume?
    - d. John Hester?

THE ARMED FORCES

1. **What do the initials R.E.M.E. stand for?**
    Is it:
    - a. Royal Electrical and Mechanical Engineers?
    - b. Royal Engineers and Maintenance Executives?
    - c. Royal Engineers and Marine Engineers?
    - d. Royal Electrical and Mobile Engineers?
2. **If you saw this badge on a soldier's epaulette, what would his rank be?**

    - a. Colonel?
    - b. Brigadier?
    - c. General?
    - d. Field-Marshal?

3. **What replaced the Royal Army Service Corps in 1965? Was it:**
    - a. The Royal Catering Corps?
    - b. The Royal Corps of Transport?
    - c. The Royal Army Ordnance Corps?
    - d. The Royal Corps de Ballet?
4. **Which branch of the British army is known as 'the Gunners'?**
    Is it:
    - a. The Royal Armoured Corps?
    - b. The Royal Engineers?
    - c. The Royal Artillery?
    - d. The Royal Corps of Signals?
5. **If you saw this badge on a soldier's epaulette, what would his rank be?**

    - a. Second Lieutenant?
    - b. Sergeant?
    - c. Captain?
    - d. Major?

N

6. **When was the Corps of the Royal Marines founded?**
   Was it in:

   a. 1664?
   b. 1764?
   c. 1864?
   d. 1964?

7. **What are the Royal Navy's three Base Ports in Great Britain?**
   Are they:

   a. Portsmouth, Plymouth and Rosyth?
   b. Portsmouth, Dover and Hull?
   c. Portsmouth, Bristol and Liverpool?
   d. Portsmouth, Margate and Rosyth?

8. **What would be the rank of a naval officer who wore these stripes on his coat sleeve?**

   a. Admiral?
   b. Rear-Admiral?
   c. Vice-Admiral?
   d. Admiral of the Fleet?

9. **The Army rank of Colonel is the equivalent of the Royal Navy rank of Captain. What is the Royal Air Force equivalent?**
   Is it:

   a. Air Commodore?
   b. Wing Commander?
   c. Squadron Leader?
   d. Group Captain?

10. **What are the names of the three Commands of the Royal Air Force in the United Kingdom?**
    Are they:

    a. Strike, Fighter and Reinforcement?
    b. Strike, Support and Training?
    c. Strike, Research and Catering?
    d. Fighter, Rescue and Attack?

1. **On British television who created the part of Dr. Finlay in** *Dr. Finlay's Casebook*?
   Was it:
   - a. Andrew Cruickshank?
   - b. John Alderton?
   - c. Nigel Stock?
   - d. Bill Simpson?

2. **Who wrote** *The General Theory of Employment, Interest and Money*?
   Was it:
   - a. J. K. Galbraith?
   - b. J. M. Keynes?
   - c. R. Opie?
   - d. R. D. Lipsey?

3. **What is a thar?**
   Is it:
   - a. A unit of heat?
   - b. A Nepalese antelope?
   - c. A Burmese coin?
   - d. A severe thunderstorm?

4. **In soccer who won the UEFA Cup Winners' Cup in 1973?**
   Was it:
   - a. Dynamo Zagreb?
   - b. Borussia Moenchengladbach?
   - c. Liverpool?
   - d. Barcelona?

5. **For what do the initials E.C.T. stand?**
   Is it:
   - a. Electrocardiogram?
   - b. Electromyography?
   - c. Electro-convulsive-therapy?
   - d. Epileptic Cure Treatment?

6. **If you were taken to Tyburn, what might you fear? That:**
   a. You were going to be executed?
   b. The tax inspector wanted to see you?
   c. You had to have your appendix removed?
   d. You were about to be married?

7. **What are the dates of the Tudor Period? Are they:**
   a. 1400 to 1485?
   b. 1485 to 1603?
   c. 1603 to 1666?
   d. 1666 to 1711?

8. **What is the name given to the system of musical notation devised by Miss Glover of Norwich in the 1840s? Is it:**
   a. A. B, C, D, E, F, G?
   b. The Glover Scale?
   c. The Tonic Sol-Fa?
   d. The Norwich Notation?

9. **Who would use a theodolite? Would it be:**
   a. A doctor?
   b. A fishmonger?
   c. A clergyman?
   d. A surveyor?

10. **When was the Suez Canal opened? Was it in:**
    a. 1750?
    b. 1869?
    c. 1901?
    d. 1949?

BRITAIN'S TOP TOWNS

London is the largest city of Great Britain. Here is a list of the towns and cities that follow London in terms of the size of their population:

Coventry
Glasgow
Cardiff
Leicester
Stoke-on-Trent
Bristol
Liverpool
Belfast
Nottingham
Kingston-upon-Hull
Newcastle-upon-Tyne
Birmingham
Leeds
Sheffield
Manchester
Edinburgh
Bradford

Can you put the list in the right order, with the city with the largest population at the top?

1. **What is the name of the institution designed by Christopher Wren and opened in 1694 for invalid soldiers?**
    Is it:
    - a. The Royal Infirmary?
    - b. The Royal Hospital, Chelsea?
    - c. St. Thomas's Hospital?
    - d. Guy's Hospital?
2. **Where is the French Foreign Office situated in Paris?**
    Is it in:
    - a. Place de la Concorde?
    - b. Avenue Wagram?
    - c. Champs Elysées?
    - d. Quai d'Orsay?
3. **What is the name of the famous public school in Windsor that was founded in 1440?**
    Is it:
    - a. Gordonstoun?
    - b. Winchester?
    - c. Charterhouse?
    - d. Eton?
4. **Where will you find Nahum?**
    Is it:
    - a. A city in Egypt?
    - b. A character in Dickens' novel *Oliver Twist*?
    - c. Part of a poppy?
    - d. One of the books of the Minor Prophets in the Old Testament?

5. **To protect the English coast during which war were the Martello Towers erected?**
   Was it during:
   - a. The Punic Wars?
   - b. The Napoleonic Wars?
   - c. The Wars of the Roses?
   - d. The First World War?

6. **What is a heliotrope?**
   Is it:
   - a. A kind of hot air balloon?
   - b. A sweet-scented plant?
   - c. A part of a car's engine?
   - d. A type of fishing rod?

7. **Between 1754 and 1956 to which village did people go for a runaway marriage?**
   Was it:
   - a. Eastry in Kent?
   - b. Steep in Hampshire?
   - c. Gretna Green in Dumfries?
   - d. Lostwithiel in Cornwall?

8. **In what year were the Dead Sea Scrolls uncovered?**
   Was it in:
   - a. 4 BC?
   - b. 1172?
   - c. 1947?
   - d. 1965?

9. **How many old pennies go into a new penny?**
   Is it:
   - a. Exactly 1?
   - b. 1.2?
   - c. 2.4?
   - d. 5?

10. **What was the title given to the eldest sons of the Kings of France from 1349 until the French Revolution?**
    Was it:
    - a. Fils?
    - b. Jeune Roi?
    - c. Dauphin?
    - d. Roi Soleil?

DECORATIONS AND MEDALS

1. **Which decoration was instituted in 1856 and originally struck from the metal of guns captured at Sebastopol during the Crimean War.**
   Was it:
   - a. The Victoria Cross?
   - b. The George Cross?
   - c. The Military Cross?
   - d. The Conspicuous Gallantry Medal?

2. **If you were awarded the G.M. what decoration would you have received? Would it be:**
   - a. The Gallantry Medal?
   - b. The Grand Military Medal?
   - c. The George Medal?
   - d. The Greek Medal?

3. **Which decoration, intended for civilians and instituted in 1940, is worn before all others except the V.C.?**
   Is it:
   - a. The Distinguished Service Order?
   - b. The Conspicuous Gallantry Medal?
   - c. The Distinguished Service Medal?
   - d. The George Cross?

4. **In 1866 a decoration was instituted for gallantry in saving life at sea or on land. What was it called?**
   Was it:
   - a. The Victoria Cross?
   - b. The Victoria Medal?
   - c. The Albert Cross?
   - d. The Albert Medal?

5. **To receive the D.S.M. to which branch of the armed services must you belong? Is it:**
   - a. The Royal Navy?
   - b. The Royal Marines?
   - c. The Army?
   - d. The Royal Air Force?

1. **The Long-playing Record was first introduced in 1948.**
    Who invented it?
    Was it:
    - a. Peter Goldmark?
    - b. Cyril Polydor?
    - c. Arnold Appleton?
    - d. Gerald Garnier?
2. **What is a 'normal' pulse rate?**
    Is it:
    - a. 60 per minute?
    - b. 72 per minute?
    - c. 80 per minute?
    - d. 92 per minute?
3. **Where and when did the first ever motor race take**
    place?
    Was it in:
    - a. France in 1894?
    - b. England in 1906?
    - c. Canada in 1909?
    - d. Germany in 1913?
4. **When was the Royal Air Force formed?**
    Was it on:
    - a. New Year's Day 1900?
    - b. Easter Monday 1914?
    - c. April Fool's Day 1918?
    - d. Boxing Day 1923?
5. **Who wrote** *Lolita***?**
    Was it:
    - a. V. S. Naipaul?
    - b. Vladimir Nabokov?
    - c. Norman Mailer?
    - d. John Dos Passos?

6. **What was the maximum speed of the Spitfire fighter plane?**
   Was it:
   - a. 175 m.p.h.?
   - b. 375 m.p.h.?
   - c. 675 m.ph.?
   - d. 1,075 m.p.h.?

7. **What is the BBC's longest-running television programme?**
   Is it:
   - a. *Crossroads*?
   - b. *Horizon*?
   - c. *Panorama*?
   - d. *Steptoe and Son*?

8. **What is another English name for the Linden tree?**
   Is it:
   - a. Almond?
   - b. Lime?
   - c. Maple?
   - d. Laburnum?

9. **What is a collection of badgers called?**
   Is it:
   - a. A pack?
   - b. A herd?
   - c. A cete?
   - d. A squad?

10. **Where is the world's longest ship canal?**
    Is it at:
    - a. Gota in Sweden?
    - b. Suez in Egypt?
    - c. Kiel in Germany?
    - d. Panama in America?

COMPOSERS

1. **He lived from 1874 to 1934 and composed a suite called** *The Planets.* **What was his name?**
   Was it:
       a. Hans Werner Henze?
       b. Gustav Holst?
       c. Paul Hindemith?
       d. Ralph Vaughan Williams?

2. **What was the name of the composer who described** *The Dream of Gerontius* **as 'the best of me'?**
   Was it:
       a. Benjamin Britten?
       b. John Ireland?
       c. Michael Tippett?
       d. Edward Elgar?

3. **What was the name of the composer whose first opera,** *Orfeo,* **was produced in 1607?**
   Was it:
       a. Monteverdi?
       b. Verdi?
       c. Mozart?
       d. Cavalli?

4. **Who lived from 1732 to 1809 and composed at least 104 symphonies?**
   Was it:
       a. Bach?
       b. Beethoven?
       c. Handel?
       d. Haydn?

5. **He was a Norwegian who lived from 1843 to 1907 and whose best known work is probably the incidental music he wrote for** *Peer Gynt.* **What was his name? Was it:**
   - a. Grieg?
   - b. Sibelius?
   - c. Neilsen?
   - d. Gluck?

6. **His sixth symphony is called the** *Pathétique.* **What's his name? Is it:**
   - a. Brahms?
   - b. Debussy?
   - c. Schubert?
   - d. Tchaikovsky?

7. **Who wrote the opera** *Rienzi***? Was it:**
   - a. Gounod?
   - b. Mozart?
   - c. Puccini?
   - d. Wagner?

8. **Who is famous for his Water and Fireworks Music? Is it:**
   - a. Mendelssohn?
   - b. Palestrina?
   - c. Handel?
   - d. Haydn?

9. **Who lived from 1874 to 1951 and revolutionised Western music with his twelve-note theory? Was it:**
   - a. John Cage?
   - b. Arnold Schoenberg?
   - c. Anton Webern?
   - d. Alban Berg?

10. **In 1923 which English composer wrote a piece for speaker and chamber orchestra called** *Facade***? Was it:**
    - a. Sir Arnold Bax?
    - b. Sir Arthur Bliss?
    - c. Sir Hubert Parry?
    - d. Sir William Walton?

ALLSORTS

1. **Who starred in the film** *The Sunshine Boys*?
   Was it:
   a. Jack Benny and Dean Martin?
   b. Bob Hope and Bing Crosby?
   c. George Burns and Walter Matthau?
   d. Tony Curtis and Jerry Lewis?

3. **Why was Bertrand Russell famous?**
   Was he:
   a. A philosopher?
   b. A mathematician?
   c. A campaigner against nuclear weapons?
   d. A winner of the Nobel Prize for Literature?

3. **Who discovered the tomb of Tutankhamun in 1922?**
   Was it:
   a. William Joyce?
   b. Howard Carter?
   c. Alec Rose?
   d. Henry Tizard?

4. **What is the capital of Niger?**
   Is it:
   a. Lagos?
   b. Bissau?
   c. Port Louis?
   d. Niamey?

5. **Who wrote** *Les Misérables*?
   Was it:
   a. Alphonse Daudet?
   b. Victor Hugo?
   c. Gustave Flaubert?
   d. Benjamin Constant?

6. **Who was killed at Khartoum in 1885?**
   Was it:
   - a. General Haig?
   - b. General Gordon?
   - c. General French?
   - d. General Johnson?

7. **Who founded London's Mermaid Theatre?**
   Was it:
   - a. Sir Laurence Olivier?
   - b. Sir Lewis Casson?
   - c. Sir Bernard Miles?
   - d. Sir Richard Attenborough?

8. **Who resigned as the Chairman of British Rail in 1976?**
   Was it:
   - a. Lord Beeching?
   - b. Sir Monty Finniston?
   - c. Lord Ryder?
   - d. Sir Richard Marsh?

9. **How many yards are there in a chain?**
   Is it:
   - a. 3?
   - b. 10?
   - c. 22?
   - d. 144?

10. **What is a brandreth?**
    Is it:
    - a. A wooden stand for casks?
    - b. A type of woolly cardigan?
    - c. A punctuation mark?
    - d. A walking encyclopedia?

WHAT'S THIS?

1. What's this?
Is it:
   a. The Pont du Gard Aqueduct at Nimes in France?
   b. The Golden Gate Bridge at San Francisco in the United States?
   c. The Bridge of Sighs at Venice in Italy?
   d. The Clifton Suspension Bridge at Bristol in England?

2. What's this?
Is it:
   a. The Royal Lodge at Windsor in England?
   b. The Petit Trianon at Versailles in France?
   c. The Palazzo della Signoria at Florence in Italy?
   d. The Town Hall at Accrington in England?

3. What's this?
Is it:
   a. St Peter's in Rome in Italy?
   b. Westminster Abbey in London in England?
   c. The Sacré Coeur in Paris in France?
   d. St Paul's in London in England?

4. What's this?
Is it:
   a. The Alhambra in Grenada in Spain?
   b. The mosque of St Sophia in Constantinople?
   c. The Taj Mahal in India?
   d. The Empire State Building in New York?

5. What's this?
Is it:
   a. St Martin's in the Fields in London in England?
   b. The Opera House in Paris in France?
   c. The Colosseum in Rome in Italy?
   d. The Parthenon in Athens in Greece?

207

1000 ANSWERS

ALLSORTS page 13
1. Mistletoe
2. Paper
3. In the Greek alphabet
4. Pierre Trudeau
5. Thomas Telford
6. John Tenniel
7. Edward I
8. Blackpool
9. Sidney Webb
10. 1964

THE GREAT EXPLORERS
page 15
1. John Cabot
2. Captain Roald Amundsen
3. William Janszoon
4. Edwin Aldrin
5. Sir Vivian Fuchs *and* Sir
   Edmund Hilary
6. Eric the Red
7. *The Golden Hind*
8. Leif Ericsson
9. Abel Tasman
10. Nicolo Polo *and* Maffeo
    Polo

ALLSORTS page 17
1. Sir Francis Galton
2. Frank Finlay
3. Theocritus
4. Hilda
5. All four! Frank Richards,
   Owen Conquest and Frank
   Drake were just three of
   Charles Hamilton's
   pseudonyms
6. Monet
7. New Zealand
8. 1895
9. Sean O'Casey
10. A kind of bird

WHEN WAS IT? page 19
1. 1789
2. 1215
3. 1924
4. 1815
5. 1959
6. 1180 BC
7. 1306
8. 1968
9. 1429
10. 1851

ALLSORTS page 21
1. Julius Nyere
2. 1646
3. Sir George Thomson
4. Johnny Carson
5. Christopher Marlowe
6. St. Augustine
7. 1959
8. Daily Express
9. Someone who relapses
   into crime
10. Puerto Rico

GREAT BATTLES page 23
1. The Battle of Agincourt
2. The Battle of Balaclava
3. The Battle of Culloden
4. The Battle of Marston
   Moor
5. The Battle of Stalingrad
6. The Battle of Lewes
7. The Battle of Omdurman
8. The Battle of Thermopylae
9. The Battle of Jutland
10. The Battle of Bannockburn

ALLSORTS page 25
1. 1964
2. John Clare
3. West Germany
4. Lord Protector
5. Tirana
6. Red Rum
7. Cucumbers
8. Corneille
9. Indira Gandhi
10. 1964

A FOR ALPHA page 27
1. Foxtrot
2. Golf
3. November
4. Oscar
5. Quebec
6. Romeo
7. Tango
8. Uniform
9. Yankee
10. Zulu

ALLSORTS page 29
1. A. A. Milne
2. About 864,000 miles
3. Behold!
4. Mormonism
5. Henry Cooper
6. In Australia
7. 1401
8. William Joyce
9. Patrick White
10. In 1935

ALL CREATURES GREAT AND SMALL page 31
1. A shrew
2. A sloth
3. A tapir
4. A platypus
5. A kiwi
6. A sparrow
7. A lobster
8. A lamprey
9. A scaly ant-eater
10. A rat

ALLSORTS page 33
1. Somerset Maugham
2. Alec Rose
3. Claudius
4. Dustin Hofmann
5. Purple-brown
6. Hilaire Belloc
7. 1515
8. Samuel Crompton
9. To Belgium
10. Sir Rowland Hill

THE COMMONWEALTH page 35
1. Australia, Canada, Newfoundland, New Zealand and South Africa
2. Thirty-three
3. South Africa
4. Nyasaland and Basutoland
5. Pakistan
6. Rhodesia, since Ian Smith's Declaration of Independence has never been recognised
7. All republics
8. Gibraltar
9. Always the Queen
10. About 950 million

ALLSORTS page 37
1. Derby County
2. 1855
3. 15 August 1945
4. 24
5. Calm
6. Audrey Hepburn
7. General Robert E. Lee
8. Sir Charles Hallé
9. Sir Anthony Van Dyck
10. A long letter

WHO WROTE IT? page 39
1. Arnold Bennett
2. Sir Thomas Malory
3. W. S. Gilbert
4. Robert Louis Stevenson
5. Frederick Marryat
6. William Langland
7. Mary Ann Evans *and* George Eliot, since the latter is the former's pseudonym
8. A. E. Housman
9. John Milton
10. Ben Jonson

ALLSORTS page 41
1. A quaver
2. Switzerland has never been a member of the United Nations
3. Laurence Harvey
4. Wat Tyler
5. Lord Montgomery
6. Godwin Austen *and* K2, since they are different names for the same mountain
7. 1959
8. The Jupiter
9. Samuel Morse
10. Nellie Melba

LINGUISTICS page 43
1. A rearrangement of the letters in a word to form another word
2. Where you mix up the initial letters of words
3. Deliberate understatement
4. A word that sounds the same as another word but has a different meaning
5. The pronouncing of two successive vowels in a word as separate sounds
6. A word that reads the same forwards as backwards
7. Likening one thing to another
8. Exaggeration
9. The use of words that begin with or include the same letters or sounds
10. The study of the origins of words

ALLSORTS page 45
1. The Lyttleton
2. Florence Nightingale
3. Jo Grimond
4. Kenneth Grahame
5. The Christmas Rose
6. Colin Cowdrey
7. Sean Connery
8. Matthew Webb
9. Kurt Weil
10. Michael Foot

POSTMAN'S LONDON page 47
1. Fleet Street
2. Earls Court
3. Muswell Hill
4. Tooting
5. Paddington
6. Chiswick
7. Kensington
8. Tottenham
9. Bow
10. South Kensington

ALLSORTS page 49
1. William Harvey
2. Excommunicate her
3. A kind of tax
4. Abraham Lincoln
5. Saint Patrick
6. A kilt
7. Sir Barnes Wallis
8. In Cheshire
9. Chuter Ede
10. Arthur Quiller-Couch

WHAT'S HIS NAME? page 51
1. Attila
2. St. Anselm
3. Benjamin Franklin
4. Walt Whitman
5. James Keir Hardie
6. Sir Henry Irving
7. William Grace
8. Sigmund Freud
9. George Fox
10. Simon Bolivar

ALLSORTS page 53
1. David Niven
2. Secretary-General of the United Nations
3. His poetry
4. Melbourne
5. Nicholas II
6. Samuel Pepys
7. Evelyn Waugh
8. Her singing
9. A type of small bird
10. 36

HISTORIC ACTS OF PARLIAMENT page 55
1. Introduce secondary education for all
2. Make the King of England Supreme Head of the Church
3. Unite England and Scotland
4. Introduce old age pensions for the first time
5. Restrict the powers of the House of Lords
6. Establish freedom of worship
7. Legalise the rule of Oliver Cromwell
8. Prohibit the employment of women, girls and boys under ten in mines
9. Force the clergy to use the English Prayer Book
10. Impose a tax on legal documents issued within the colonies

ALLSORTS page 57
1. *No Man's Land*
2. A sleeveless coat of mail
3. Hugh Gaitskell
4. 1625
5. 2.9 miles
6. The Roman god Janus
7. On 21 or 22 June
8. For his running
9. *Don Giovanni*
10. The 50p piece

THE EARTH page 59
1. About 6,588 million million million tons
2. About 197 million square miles
3. About seven-tenths
4. The fifth largest planet
5. About 93,000,000 miles
6. Asia
7. About a half
8. Trebled
9. England *and* Bangladesh
10. Europe

ALLSORTS page 61
1. Aston Villa
2. Snakes
3. Italy
4. Elizabeth Garrett Anderson
5. Dorothy
6. Arthur Balfour
7. Irving Berlin
8. Thomas Bowdler
9. Samuel Butler
10. Richard Chamberlain

ENGLISH MONARCHS page 63
1. Hardicanute
2. Henry II
3. Elizabeth I
4. Edward IV
5. Stephen
6. Edward VII
7. 325 days
8. George I
9. Henry III ·
10. 1483

ALLSORTS page 65
1. Nelson Rockefeller
2. Robespierre
3. Frederick Sanger
4. George Sand
5. 1606
6. Harry Corbett
7. Existentialism
8. P. G. Wodehouse
9. A painter
10. John Wesley

SCIENCE page 67

1. To measure height above the earth
2. A unit of length
3. Approximately equal to
4. Fe
5. A proton
6. Direct current
7. An alkali
8. The coil of an electric motor or dynamo
9. Calculus
10. Au

ALLSORTS page 69

1. 1327
2. Croesus
3. A word spelt like another word but with a different meaning
4. *Tom Jones*
5. Cliff Michelmore
6. Gabriel Fahrenheit
7. Burned down
8. Vasco da Gama
9. 7.00 am
10. A writer

INTERNATIONAL CURRENCIES page 71

1. Albania
2. Thailand
3. Panama
4. Brazil
5. Zambia
6. Haiti
7. Poland
8. Greece
9. The Netherlands
10. All four!

ALLSORTS page 73

1. The White Ensign
2. An architect
3. Between East Finchley and Morden in London
4. His ice skating
5. 4 minutes 12.75 seconds
6. William Wordsworth
7. Furniture
8. Viscount Slim
9. 1904
10. Albert Finney

ISLANDS page 75

1. Australia
2. The Arctic
3. 84,186 square miles
4. Borneo
5. Great Britain
6. Jersey
7. Ceylon
8. The Channel Islands
9. New Zealand
10. The Isle of Man

ALLSORTS page 77

1. Both have been Astronomer Royal
2. Konrad Adenauer
3. A beautiful woman
4. Typhoid Fever
5. Thomas Arne
6. Nancy Astor
7. An actor-manager
8. She was burnt at the stake
9. 1833
10. Dacca

ABBREVIATIONS page 79

1. Advanced Passenger Train
2. British Army of the Rhine
3. Cambridge
4. Dame Commander of the Order of the British Empire
5. Kelvin
6. Master of the Foxhounds
7. Prisoner of War
8. Talbot House
9. Union of Soviet Socialist Republics
10. Venerable

ALLSORTS page 81
1. Proserpine
2. 4.5434
3. Bobby Moore
4. Boris Spassky
5. Richard Burton
6. A monkey
7. John Wilkes Booth
8. The kaleidoscope
9. Chou En-Lai
10. 51 BC

INVENTORS page 83
1. Blaise Pascal
2. Robert von Bunsen
3. Hermann Dreser
4. John Napier
5. Robert Watson-Watt
6. Galileo Galilei
7. Alexander Graham Bell
8. William Oughtred
9. Hans Lippershey
10. Wallace Carothers

ALLSORTS page 85
1. John Constable
2. A small mug
3. Mark Twain
4. X-rays
5. A playwright
6. 1846
7. Pietro Annigoni
8. 1955
9. A philosopher
10. Voltaire

CAPITAL CITIES page 87
1. Jerusalem
2. Budapest
3. Valetta
4. Rangoon
5. Kinshasa
6. Quito
7. Hamilton
8. Rabat
9. Montevideo
10. Suva

ALLSORTS page 89
1. 1955
2. Samuel Richardson
3. 1946
4. An American bird
5. Cotton
6. They have all been Poet Laureate
7. 'Happy Birthday To You'
8. 1399
9. 1.016
10. J. E. Lundstom

TOP CITIES page 91
New York
Tokyo
Shanghai
Buenos Aires
Mexico City
Peking
London
Moscow
Los Angeles
Chicago
Sao Paulo
Bombay
Seoul
Cairo
Philadelphia
Djakarta
Rio de Janeiro
Tientsin
Detroit
Delhi

ALLSORTS page 92
1. Oklahoma in 1935
2. 98.4°F
3. British Boxing Champions
4. The Wellington
5. Plato
6. Philip V of Spain
7. Anseriformes
8. Eleven
9. Sirius
10. Edgar Allan Poe

TOP TONGUES page 94
Mandarin Chinese
English
Russian
Hindi
Spanish
German
Japanese
Bengali
Arabic
Portuguese
French
Malay
Italian
Urdu
Cantonese Chinese
Javanese
Ukrainian
Telegu
Wu Chinese
Tamil

ALLSORTS page 95
1. A mixed dish
2. Leonard Bernstein
3. Corsica
4. Macbeth
5. Izaak Walton
6. 32°
7. Bacchus
8. Tito
9. An opera singer
10. Bangkok

BRITISH PRIME MINISTERS
page 97
1. The Duke of Wellington
2. Stanley Baldwin
3. 1963
4. Viscount Melbourne
5. 1721
6. Sir Harold Wilson
7. 1868
8. The Liberal Party
9. David Lloyd George
10. Spencer Perceval

ALLSORTS page 99
1. Oxford
2. Titian
3. The Severn
4. A flat-topped hill
5. Fly the English Channel
6. Anton Chekhov
7. Jakob and Wilhelm
8. A runner
9. About 700,000 miles
10. William of Wykeham

WHAT DID HE DO? page 101
1. Cross the Niagara Falls on
   a tightrope
2. Initiate the fourth Crusade
3. A cabinet maker
4. Raise the Highlands in
   support of Charles I and
   Charles II
5. Discover oxygen
6. A Dutch philosopher
7. Build lighthouses
8. A pirate who was hanged
   at Execution Dock
9. A racing driver who held
   land and water speed
   records
10. An American novelist

ALLSORTS page 103
1. Impressionism
2. Thou shalt have no other
   God but Me
3. 17 March
4. Knight of the Thistle
5. Rudolph
6. Roman Emperors
7. 1956
8. The area of a circle
9. The safety pin
10. A fox

OCEANS AND SEAS page 105
1. The Pacific Ocean
2. 35,948 feet
3. 12,451 feet
4. About 140 million square miles
5. None of them!
6. The Malay Sea
7. It is made up of a series of other seas, gulfs and straits
8. The Caribbean Sea
9. The Baltic Sea
10. A sea surrounded by land

ALLSORTS page 107
1. Victor Emmanuel II
2. Celtic
3. Jane Austen
4. Graham Sutherland
5. A Spanish coin
6. Jonathan Swift
7. Mandalay
8. David Bowie
9. 1949
10. A poet

MYTHOLOGY page 109
1. Venus
2. Adonis
3. Daphne
4. Icarus
5. Parnassus
6. Narcissus
7. Romulus
8. Menelaus
9. The Graces
10. Poseidon

ALLSORTS page 111
1. A kind of snuff
2. 1760
3. Tobias Smollett
4. C. P. Snow
5. Rommel
6. Ovid
7. *The Merry Wives of Windsor*
8. Louis Lumière
9. Three
10. 1773

SPACE TRAVEL page 113
1. Vostok I
2. Sheppard
3. In 1963
4. Leonov
5. Gemini 8
6. Collins
7. Eagle
8. Skylab
9. White
10. Helios 1

ALLSORTS page 115
1. Thirteen
2. John Nash
3. Sinclair Lewis
4. A prehistoric horse
5. Rolls-Royce
6. Julie Andrews
7. David Livingstone
8. 6.21
9. Zomba
10. Joe Orton

MUSICAL TERMS page 117
1. Fast, but not too fast
2. Becoming quieter and slower
3. With verve and dash
4. Gracefully
5. In a smooth style
6. Slow
7. Very fast
8. In a whisper
9. Lively
10. At walking pace

ALLSORTS page 119
1. James I
2. 100.5°F
3. Henry Ford
4. Friedrich Froebel
5. William Tell
6. A great ballet dancer
7. C. S. Forester
8. R. A. Butler
9. Kruschev
10. Mohammed

WEIGHTS AND MEASURES
page 121
1. Ten
2. Sixteen
3. 2.54
4. 640
5. Eight
6. 6,080
7. 1.136
8. 2,240
9. 1,728
10. 1,609

ALLSORTS page 123
1. Benjamin Franklin
2. The Peloponnesian War
3. Trygve Lie
4. Sebastian Cabot
5. Edinburgh
6. Guallatiri
7. Bechuanaland
8. Air Chief Marshal
9. Cu
10. A chord

MOTORCARS page 125
1. Model T Ford
2. Lamborghini Mark III
3. Fiat 128 Coupé
4. Rolls-Royce Silver Ghost
5. Citroën GS
6. Peugeot Bébé
7. Morris Cowley
8. Lotus Elite
9. Du Pont Model G
10. 3-litre Bentley

ALLSORTS page 127
1. Marx
2. Ho Chi Minh City
3. Enid Blyton
4. Edmond Rostand
5. Yorkshire
6. *Wuthering Heights*
7. 20,000
8. Joseph Bramah
9. Rupert Brooke
10. Honor Blackman

LATIN TAGS page 129
1. Time flies
2. Which was to be proved
3. Never despair
4. By way of example
5. By the grace of God
6. Love conquers all
7. Here and everywhere
8. Whether he will or not
9. For boys and girls
10. May he rest in peace

ALLSORTS page 131
1. Donald Coggan
2. Dvorak
3. Sergei Eisenstein
4. Farouk I
5. M. Spitz
6. A kind of prayer
7. Eleanor
8. Sir Ambrose Fleming
9. Barbarossa
10. An economist

WHAT'S HER NAME? page 133
1. Louisa May Alcott
2. Dame Ellen Terry
3. Saint Teresa
4. Madame Roland
5. Emmeline Pankhurst
6. Florence Nightingale
7. Flora Macdonald
8. Nell Gwynne
9. Elizabeth Fry
10. Christina Rossetti

ALLSORTS page 135
1. A controversial discussion
2. Abelard
3. 1821
4. Allende
5. Raymond Burr
6. A Hungarian composer
7. The Venerable Bede
8. Beethoven
9. Barbara Moore
10. John Wayne

WHERE'S WHERE? page 137
1. England
2. United States of America
3. The Republic of Ireland
4. Algeria
5. France
6. Canada
7. Yugoslavia
8. England
9. Poland
10. Korea

ALLSORTS page 139
1. Greyfriars
2. 1903
3. F. E. Smith
4. Pantomime
5. 1607
6. It comes from the French *m'aidez*
7. 45°
8. William Bligh
9. Boadicea
10. Founded the Salvation Army

UNITED STATES PRESIDENTS page 141
1. 1789-1797
2. John Adams
3. Franklin Roosevelt
4. William McKinley
5. John Kennedy
6. Martin Van Buren
7. Calvin Coolidge
8. Andrew Jackson
9. 1974
10. James Buchanan

ALLSORTS page 143
1. 10 lb
2. Carbon dioxide
3. Mrs. Patrick Campbell
4. *The Eagle*
5. Loch Lomond
6. Samuel Cody
7. A pioneer of photography
8. Cecil Day Lewis
9. James Dewar
10. Italy

HOME COUNTIES page 145
1. Forty-six
2. Avon
3. Northallerton
4. Norfolk
5. Eight
6. Dyfed
7. Mid Glamorgan
8. Inverness
9. Lanark
10. Antrim

ALLSORTS page 147
1. On the seventh Sunday after Easter
2. The Sahara
3. *The Endeavour*
4. Sir Douglas Haig
5. He was killed in an air crash
6. John Gay
7. The War of the Spanish Succession
8. Timothy West
9. Coventry
10. 0.4

AMERICAN ENGLISH page 149
1. A thousand million
2. A dressing table
3. A public lavatory
4. A tap
5. Petrol
6. A queue
7. A policeman's truncheon
8. A handbag
9. An estate agent
10. A waistcoat

ALLSORTS page 151
1. Haile Selasse I
2. 100,000
3. Thomas Hardy
4. Henrietta Maria
5. Keith Holyoake
6. A chief priest
7. Henrik Ibsen
8. 1923
9. Four
10. Save Our Souls

MUSICAL INSTRUMENTS page 153
1. A cello
2. A tenor saxophone
3. A piccolo
4. A tuba
5. A spinettina
6. An oboe
7. A lute
8. The vibes
9. A trumpet
10. A mute

ALLSORTS page 155
1. A large African ape
2. Robert Kennedy
3. Juvenal
4. Jomo Kenyatta
5. His chess playing as world champion
6. 1930
7. 1961
8. Marlon Brando
9. Puccini
10. A trillion

ASTRONOMY page 157
1. 25,000,000,000,000 miles away
2. 6,000,000,000,000 miles
3. Between 2,000 and 3,000
4. Sirius
5. 864,000 miles
6. 365¼ days
7. 248.43 years
8. Mercury
9. 27 days 7 hours 43 minutes 11 seconds
10. The Great Bear

ALLSORTS page 159
1. An outstanding novel
2. Jonah Barrington
3. Twenty
4. Joseph Lister
5. 1928
6. Mountains
7. Greta Garbo
8. 1564
9. Haydn
10. Charles II

SEA TALK page 161
1. The broadest part of a ship's bottom
2. A sea measure of 100 fathoms
3. The right side of the ship looking forward
4. A type of anchor
5. A case to house a compass
6. Behind
7. The holes in a ship's sides used to drain water from the decks
8. From 4.00 pm to 8.00 pm
9. A type of rope
10. Six feet

ALLSORTS page 163
1. Judea
2. 1658
3. The Windmill
4. The Brontës
5. The I.B.A. television masts at Emley Moor *and* at Belmont
6. 186 miles
7. George Orwell
8. 1977
9. 1970
10. 14 July

INTERNATIONAL LETTERS page 165
1. Austria
2. Venezuela
3. Cuba
4. Monaco
5. Spain
6. Liechtenstein
7. Argentina
8. The Vatican City
9. Luxembourg
10. South Africa

ALLSORTS page 167
1. Louis XVIII
2. 10p
3. His record-breaking swimming
4. Famous architects
5. Marshal Stalin
6. Dougal
7. H. G. Wells
8. Mia Farrow and Danny Kaye
9. An illegal drinking place
10. The Chained Lady

SPORT page 169
1. Cassius Clay
2. Cycling
3. Win the British Open
4. West Germany
5. Table Tennis
6. The Rugby League Challenge Cup
7. Motor cycling
8. Joe Louis
9. South Africa
10. Johan Cruyff

ALLSORTS page 171
1. Trotsky
2. Anthony Trollope
3. Abel Tasman
4. 186,000 miles per second
5. *The Tatler, The Spectator* and *The Guardian*
6. Warren Beatty
7. R. B. Sheridan
8. The name of the first television satellite launched by the United States
9. 212°
10. 1651

ART AND ARTISTS page 173
1. *The Mona Lisa*
2. Raphael
3. Miniatures
4. El Greco
5. An architect
6. Michelangelo Buonarotti
7. Jackson Pollock
8. For his sculptures
9. Monet — not to be confused with Manet who painted a less well-known painting called *Déjeuner sur l'Herbe* in 1863
10. Francesco Goya

ALLSORTS page 175
1. Graham Kerr
2. Rasputin
3. A form of shorthand writing
4. Paderewski
5. John Henry Newman
6. His pocket cartoons
7. Katherine Mansfield
8. Types of cloud formation
9. Vaduz
10. Charlemagne

GET KNOTTED page 177
1. A reef knot
2. A sheet bend
3. A clove hitch
4. A sheepshank
5. A half-hitch
6. A round turn and two half-hitches
7. A timber hitch
8. A wall knot
9. A figure of eight
10. A bowline

ALLSORTS page 179
1. Writing *The Principle of Population*
2. 1,728
3. Morphine
4. Ben Nevis
5. 24 May
6. Coleridge
7. 4 BC
8. Lord Jeffreys
9. Jerome K. Jerome
10. Christianity

NEW NAMES FOR OLD page 181
1. Bélize
2. Khmer Republic
3. Lake Idi Amin Dada
4. Cape Canaveral
5. River Zaire
6. El Djezair
7. The Arab Republic of Egypt
8. El-Dar-el-Beida
9. Sri Lanka
10. The Sultanate of Oman

ALLSORTS page 183
1. The name of Peter Pan's fairy
2. William Hogarth
3. Harold II
4. Stephen Potter
5. John Donne
6. Edward Lear
7. The Savoy
8. Charlie Chaplin
9. Geoffrey Chaucer
10. Bakelite

NOBEL PRIZEWINNERS page 185
1. Alexander Solzhenitsyn
2. Le Duc Tho
3. Dorothy Hodgkin
4. Rudyard Kipling
5. Bragg
6. Chemistry
7. UNICEF
8. Linus Pauling
9. Sean MacBride for Peace
10. Economic Sciences

ALLSORTS page 187
1. The laser beam
2. Shoemaking
3. A dagger
4. William Cowper
5. Designing aircraft
6. Robert Bruce
7. Mary Baker Eddy
8. Euripides
9. For his sculpture
10. 1967

FOREIGN PHRASES page 189
1. A pen name
2. In the open air
3. A tasty morsel
4. I serve
5. Reply, please
6. Immediately
7. Enough!
8. Completely done for
9. Between ourselves
10. A false step

ALLSORTS page 191
1. A disease that poultry get
2. George and Weedon Grossmith
3. Gregory XIII
4. 1,000
5. Stonewall
6. Cyril Fletcher
7. L. P. Hartley
8. The names of winds
9. Henry III
10. Basil Hume

THE ARMED FORCES page 193
1. Royal Electrical and Mechanical Engineers
2. Field-Marshal
3. The Royal Corps of Transport
4. The Royal Artillery
5. Captain
6. 1664
7. Portsmouth, Plymouth and Rosyth
8. Admiral of the Fleet
9. Group Captain
10. Strike, Support and Training

ALLSORTS page 195
1. Bill Simpson
2. J. M. Keynes
3. A Nepalese antelope
4. Liverpool
5. Electro-convulsive-therapy
6. You were going to be executed
7. 1485 to 1603
8. The Tonic Sol-Fa
9. A surveyor
10. 1869

BRITAIN'S TOP TOWNS page 197

London	Belfast
Birmingham	Coventry
Glasgow	Newcastle-upon-Tyne
Leeds	
Liverpool	Nottingham
Sheffield	Leicester
Manchester	Kingston-upon-Hull
Bradford	
Edinburgh	Cardiff
Bristol	Stoke-on-Trent

ALLSORTS page 198
1. The Royal Hospital, Chelsea
2. Quai d'Orsay
3. Eton
4. One of the books of the Minor Prophets in the Old Testament
5. The Napoleonic Wars
6. A sweet-scented plant
7. Gretna Green in Dumfries
8. 1947
9. 2.4
10. Dauphin

DECORATIONS AND MEDALS page 200
1. The Victoria Cross
2. The George Medal
3. The George Cross
4. The Albert Medal
5. The Royal Navy or the Royal Marines

ALLSORTS page 201
1. Peter Goldmark
2. 72 per minute
3. France in 1894
4. April Fool's Day 1918
5. Vladimir Nabokov
6. 375 m.p.h.
7. *Panorama*
8. Lime
9. A cete
10. Gota in Sweden

COMPOSERS page 203
1. Gustav Holst
2. Edward Elgar
3. Monteverdi
4. Haydn
5. Grieg
6. Tchaikovsky
7. Wagner
8. Handel
9. Arnold Schoenberg
10. Sir William Walton

ALLSORTS page 205
1. George Burns and Walter Matthau
2. He was all four!
3. Howard Carter
4. Niamey
5. Victor Hugo
6. General Gordon
7. Sir Bernard Miles
8. Sir Richard Marsh
9. 22
10. A wooden stand for casks

WHAT'S THIS? page 207
1. The Pont du Gard Aqueduct at Nimes in France
2. The Petit Trianon at Versailles
3. St Paul's in London in England
4. The Taj Mahal in India
5. The Parthenon in Athens in Greece